t'ai chi at home

A practical stand-up guide to mastering the essential movements and sequences that will produce physical and mental wellbeing

PAUL CROMPTON

CARROLL & BROWN PUBLISHERS LIMITED

First published in 2003 in the United Kingdom by
Carroll & Brown Publishers Limited
20 Lonsdale Road
London NW6 6RD

Managing Editor: Michelle Bernard
Editor: Stuart Moorhouse
Designer: Justin Ford
Production Staff: Karol Davies, Nigel Reed, Paul Stradling
Photographer: Jules Selmes
Photographic Assistant: David Yems

T'AI CHI AT HOME

Text © Paul Crompton 2003

Illustrations and compilation © Carroll & Brown Ltd 2003

A CIP catalogue record for this book is available from the British Library

ISBN 1-903258-66-9

10987654321

Reproduced by Emirates
Printed and bound in Italy by Graphicom

Contents

Introduction

Foreword   4

How to Use This Book   5

History of T'ai Chi   6

Chapter 1 Understanding T'ai Chi

Internal Elements of T'ai Chi   10

External Elements of T'ai Chi   12

Chapter 2 Preparing for T'ai Chi

Arm Swing   16

Gravity Back Stretch   17

Relaxation   18

Folding Wings   20

Chapter 3 The T'ai Chi Form

Beginning   24

End   86

Chapter 4 Applications with a Partner

Single Push Hands   90

Double Push Hands   92

Complete Form at a Glance   94

Index and Acknowledgments   96

foreword

T'ai chi is a series of exercises helping to combat stress and fatigue and improve flexibility, muscle tone, and general health. It does this by enabling chi (internal energy) to move freely through the body, encouraging harmony between the body and mind.

Practicing t'ai chi keeps you aware of your body. The relaxed but steady focus is similar to many meditation practices, and t'ai chi has often been described as a "meditation in motion." Like meditation, t'ai chi helps you to calm your mind and better meet with the strains of modern life.

With regular practice, t'ai chi can reduce stress and improve your mood by naturally increasing the body's production of endorphins. After many years of practice, t'ai chi enables the nervous system to respond with an extremely heightened sensitivity to movement.

The movements of t'ai chi are learned together in a sequence known as a Form. In this book you practice a version of the Yang Family style. It was produced in the 1950s as part of a drive by the Chinese government to standardize t'ai chi training.

You don't need any prior experience to follow the Form given in this book, but your experience of t'ai chi will be greatly enhanced by finding a well-qualified teacher. If you are already taking lessons, this book will help you perfect what you have learned in class and insure that your home practice is done correctly.

how to use this book

This book has been created with a folding base so that you can stand it up in front of you while working through the exercises in the Form. The top page of each sequence contains information about the movements on the lower pages, as well as tips on posture, notes on the health benefits of practicing t'ai chi, and descriptions of variations on each position.

If you are new to t'ai chi, it is advisable to practice the exercises in the first two chapters before beginning the Form.

All you need to practice t'ai chi is some energy and focus and a peaceful place with enough space for you to stretch your body upward and outward. The area in which you choose to practice should be pleasantly warm with good ventilation. You should wear light or stretchy clothes so that your body feels unrestricted when moving, and wear shoes with soles that can slide easily across the floor.

When learning the Form, just familiarize yourself with one or two sequences, practicing them regularly. Gradually add the following postures until you have covered the entire Form.

It should take about three to five minutes to perform the complete Form and it may take about four to six months to learn all of the sequences. You will experience the benefits of the movements quite quickly after beginning to practice. Be patient. Go through the movements repeatedly so you will gradually learn them and don't hurry to finish each sequence. Perform each movement thoroughly and fully integrate it into the sequence.

history of t'ai chi

T'ai chi is an ancient Chinese art of movement. Its exact origins are hard to trace, but there are theories that t'ai chi came from a style of martial arts introduced to the Chen family by an unknown martial artist who was able to defeat all their best fighters. This seems likely, because the Chen style of t'ai chi was one in which very slow movements alternated with fast, fierce, and powerful ones—all the qualities of classical Chinese fighting arts.

But legend has it that t'ai chi was created by a seven-foot tall Taoist Immortal, called Chang San-feng, who learned it in a dream. Taoist monks have also been credited with its invention as a method of self-cultivation. While these views remain debatable, t'ai chi is undoubtedly inspired by Taoist beliefs. Taoism is a Chinese philosophy and religion concerned with understanding the Tao, the energy and movement of the entire universe. Taoism extols interacting naturally and passively with the outside world, avoiding conflict and aggression in order to achieve harmony with the Tao.

T'ai chi is studied today worldwide by practitioners from all walks of life.

The five best known t'ai chi styles are Yang, Wu (two versions), Chen, Sun, and Hao. They are all said to have originated from the original Chen style, which began in the middle of the 19th century, when Yang Lu-chan studied at the Chen village in Wen county. Around this time, t'ai chi was also known as Cotton Boxing, Soft Boxing, and Transformation Boxing.

After the Chinese revolution of 1911, the authorities summoned a wide range of martial artists to meet and codify their methods so that a national curriculum could be established. In 1955 the t'ai chi Form that was considered the most elementary and fundamental was accepted. Called the 24-Step Beijing Form, it was based largely on the Yang style and is now one of the most widely practiced t'ai chi Forms in the world. It is characterized by mainly vertical postures and relaxed movements, performed at a slow pace and complemented with calm, even breathing. This is the Form demonstrated in this book, as it is considered one of the best for introducing beginners to t'ai chi principles and its more important postures.

The number of movements in any t'ai chi Form can vary from as few as 12 to as many as 108. Where there are larger numbers of movements, these Forms include frequent repetitions of earlier movements. The repeated movements are considered the more important ones, such as Single Whip and Brush Knee and Push. This is because they are the sequences that best demonstrate the essential principles of t'ai chi. The Form shown in this book usually takes about five minutes to perform, and with regular practice is easy to memorize.

T'AI CHI FORMS

When you see people performing t'ai chi movements in parks or on television, they will usually be practicing a Form. There are several Forms in each style, and they consist of a long sequence of movements, which can take from five to fifteen minutes to complete depending on the Form.

"Who can claim to be right when speaking
Of the ways of the body?
The mind and the chi are paramount,
Bones and muscles subordinate."

From "Song of the Thirteen Postures"

As well as calming and focusing the mind, t'ai chi has many well-documented physical benefits. Among these are a lowering of the pulse rate, improved flexibility, and increased lung capacity. Knowing about these can help inspire your practice and enhance your knowledge about t'ai chi.

1

>> understanding t'ai chi

internal elements of t'ai chi

Traditional Chinese concepts, including chi, Yin and Yang, and the *dantiens*, enhance your experience and understanding of t'ai chi.

chi energy

Whether translated as intrinsic energy, vital energy, vitality, or the life force, chi figures in all Chinese arts, martial and otherwise. An acupuncturist or shiatsu practitioner aims to release, control, or free-up chi when applying treatment. In Chinese medicine, the flow of chi is essential for good health, and medical conditions are seen as an indication that there is an imbalance in the patient's chi.

Feng shui, the Chinese art of understanding the flow of chi or energy through landscapes and homes, has become very popular in the West. T'ai chi can be understood in a similar context. Just as a hill, an open space, or the sharp corner of a room affects the energy flow of an environment, so too can a posture, a gesture, or the speed of an action influence the movement of chi through someone's body. Influencing the energy flow within the body in a beneficial way is one of the most important aspects of t'ai chi.

Chi travels within the body mainly along the *chinglo* (or meridians), which lie along the surface of the skin, or sometimes deeper in the body (see illustrations page 11). As the chi travels, it passes through vital points where it can be focused, taken in, or emitted. The more important of these are known as *dantiens*. Practicing t'ai chi stimulates this vital network of chi-carrying vessels. The slow, studied movements, carried out with a deep sense of relaxation and regular rhythm, produce a state that is conducive to optimum chi flow. This improvement in the flow of chi is one of the main reasons why t'ai chi is so effective in combating stress.

yin and yang

The symbol to the left represents Yin and Yang. The concept of Yin and Yang is a way to understand the fluctuating relationships of everything in the universe. Yin represents the feminine, the earth, softness, and reciprocation. Yang represents the masculine, heat, hardness, and movement. For other aspects of Yin and Yang, see the chart, right.

The Yin and Yang symbol shows how Yang, the white sections of the symbol, flow into Yin, the dark sections. The dots of opposing colors in each swirl demonstrate that Yang always contains an element of Yin and vice versa. Yin and Yang are in a state of constant flux. However, the Yin and Yang elements should also be in harmony, or mental and physical illness can result.

T'ai chi uses the concepts of Yin and Yang in the contexts of a physical discipline and a martial art. A t'ai chi practitioner may apply a yielding Yin action to evade a Yang action, such as an aggressive strike.

YIN AND YANG QUALITIES

YIN	YANG
Female	Male
Moon	Sun
Completion	Creation
Cold	Heat
Dark	Light
Material form	Heaven
Yielding	Applying
Still	Movement
Receptivity	Initiative
Closed movements	Open movements
Palms facing down in t'ai chi movements	Palms facing up in t'ai chi movements

dantiens

Many people are now familiar with the idea of chakras—wheels or centers that are focal points of energy inside the body. The *dantiens* of t'ai chi and chi kung (general exercises for developing chi) correspond to the chakras of yoga. The name *dantien* can be translated as "a place where something precious is stored," which is chi in this case. So, *dantiens* are the places where chi can be focused and maintained, rather than diffused by thoughts, emotional upsets, and stress. The *dantien* in the lower abdomen is of primary importance because it is located inside your center of gravity. It is a place to focus on for both physical and mental balance, and as a result is often referred to as "the" *dantien*. In Zen Buddhism, one of the most well-known methods for focusing the attention is to bring your awareness to this point.

junction points

These are places along chi meridians where internal chi is emitted and external chi is received. There are a number of different junction points, but in this book we focus on the *lao-gong* points and the *ming-men* point. The *lao-gong* points found on the palms are used during t'ai chi to "direct" chi along the body. This opens meridian points and improves energy circulation (see page 52). The *ming-men* point is located beneath the kidneys, opposite the navel, and along the center of the body. It is known as the "Gate of Life." If chi cannot flow correctly through this point, it can lead to emotional difficulties. The movement Step Back and Drive Monkey Away (see page 40) is beneficial for the *ming-men*.

Key
- ● Heaven Linking Zone
- ● Upper *Dantien*
- ● Middle *Dantien*
- ● Lower *Dantien*
- ○ The Hands (The Movable zone)
- ● *Ming-men*
- ● *Lao-gong*

Dantiens   Junction Points

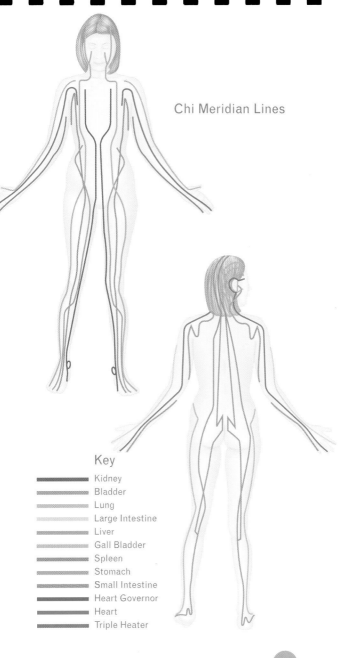

Chi Meridian Lines

Key
- ▬ Kidney
- ▬ Bladder
- ▬ Lung
- ▬ Large Intestine
- ▬ Liver
- ▬ Gall Bladder
- ▬ Spleen
- ▬ Stomach
- ▬ Small Intestine
- ▬ Heart Governor
- ▬ Heart
- ▬ Triple Heater

external elements of t'ai chi

While t'ai chi is a flexible art, not a rigid system of rules, there are certain fundamental ideas regarding physical movement and posture that must be upheld while practicing the t'ai chi Form.

posture

In the Yang style of t'ai chi, your body is in an upright posture during most of the Form. When you are practicing this Form with your feet flat on the floor, you should feel "rooted" into the earth. This can be achieved in a number of ways. One is to become aware of the pull of gravity on your body. At the same time, you should also imagine a natural force of "anti-gravity" pulling your neck and head upward in gentle opposition to the pull of gravity. These two actions can ease stress on the vertebrae.

tension and relaxation

An important component of t'ai chi is the controlled use of gradual tension and relaxation. If you were to make a clenched fist with your right hand, you would probably do it in one quick movement. Most people perform all their movements this way. However, if you were to clench your fist slowly, gradually moving from a relaxed, open hand, to a contracted, closed hand, taking about six seconds to do so, and then opened your hand in the same way, gradually

releasing the tension over six seconds, your movements would begin to assume the precise control of your body that t'ai chi requires. Through t'ai chi, you can use this method of slowly tensing and relaxing to gain a heightened appreciation of how your whole body moves.

hand positions

To be thorough in your performance and understanding of t'ai chi, you need to appreciate the importance of the position of your hands. In general, your hands should be held apart, in a slightly curved position, as though holding a basketball. Your fingers should be a couple of inches apart. Keep the area between the first finger and thumb open, creating the space known in t'ai chi as the "Tiger's Mouth." As you become proficient at t'ai chi, you can introduce a more sensitive use of your hands into your movements, using the concepts of Yin and Yang. As you begin a movement, relax your hands, closing them slightly (a Yin movement). Then, as you move through a sequence, such as Push, you gradually tighten and spread your hands (a Yang movement).

opening and closing

The phrase "opening and closing" helps to clarify the concept of Yin and Yang in t'ai chi. Yang is an opening movement and Yin a closing movement. As you perform the t'ai chi Form, feel how your joints open and close. If you stand in the "Bow Stance" (see right), with your left leg bent in front and bearing most of your weight, you feel what appears to be a contradiction. Your left leg is bent, which is a more closed movement (Yin), but the same leg is bearing the weight, so it is exerting force (Yang). Your right leg is more open (Yang), but bearing less weight (Yin). We begin in this example to see some of the subtleties of Yin and Yang, where one part of a movement can be Yin and another part can be Yang simultaneously.

the "bow stance"

This is an essential movement that recurs throughout the Form, so spend time practicing the correct position for the "Bow Stance." In the diagram on the right, the feet are hip-width apart, with one foot pointing directly ahead, and the other pointing away from it an angle. This movement is used in t'ai chi more than any other, and it is important that you can perform it correctly and comfortably.

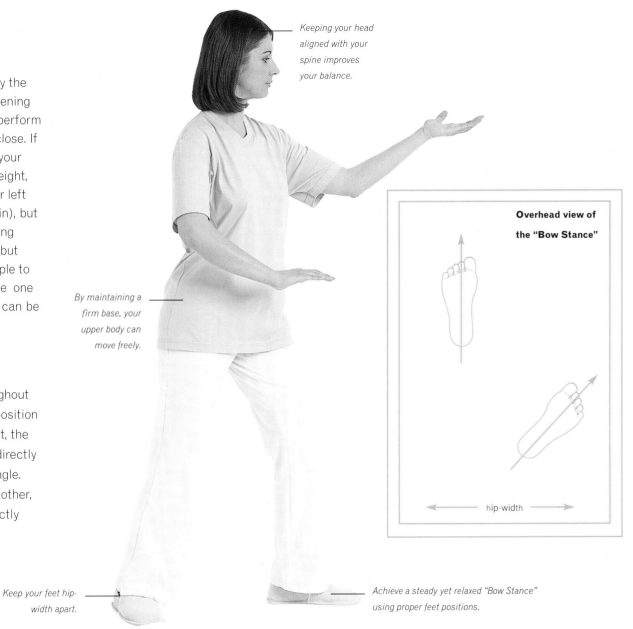

Keeping your head aligned with your spine improves your balance.

By maintaining a firm base, your upper body can move freely.

Keep your feet hip-width apart.

Achieve a steady yet relaxed "Bow Stance" using proper feet positions.

Overhead view of the "Bow Stance"

hip-width

"The tail bone should be upright
So that the spirit may rise to the crown of the head.
And to cause the body to be agile and lively
Suspend the head as if by a single hair."

From "Song of the Thirteen Postures"

When preparing for t'ai chi, remember how important it is to focus your mind on what your body is doing. These exercises help unify your mind with your body's movements. They also help you to relax. The founder of modern Yang style t'ai chi, Yang Cheng-fu, is reputed to have said in reply to almost all questions about his art: "Relax, relax, just relax."

2

>> preparing for t'ai chi

arm swing

This exercise helps you to develop relaxed shoulders and loose, but controlled, arm movements. If your shoulders and arms are relaxed, chi will flow easily, you will be able to turn your head freely, and you will benefit from the improved flow of energy throughout your body.

ARM SWING >>

1 Stand with your feet hip-width apart, your left foot forward and turned outward. Place your left forearm behind your back, fist lightly clenched. Swing your right arm freely forward and back until your shoulder feels loosened and relaxed.

After you have completed steps 1 to 3, change your stance (move your right leg forward and your left back), and practice the arm swing with your other arm.

2 Lift your arm up in front of you using the momentum of the swing from step 1. Don't use the muscles on the top of your shoulder and arm to lift your arm. If you use these muscles and tense up, the joint will begin to freeze.

3 Let your arm travel all the way up so your elbow bends and your hand slaps down at the top of your back. You should find that you can move your arm back further than you could if you used just your muscles to reach behind you.

gravity back stretch

This exercise can rectify the tendency many people have of tensing their neck muscles. This habit is detrimental to your t'ai chi practice and adversely affects your posture, breathing, and mood.

GRAVITY BACK STRETCH >>

1 Slowly relax the muscles at the back of your neck, lowering your head as far as possible without feeling uncomfortable. At the same time, gently let go of your arms and shoulders, letting them "spread."

While the physical movement of Gravity Back Stretch may appear simple, you need to pay extremely close attention to how your body is moving in order to get the most out of this exercise.

2 Gradually sink as far forward as you can. With practice you will feel a beneficial stretch in your back muscles. Gravity is acting on your back, through your head, shoulders, and arms, so you are being naturally stretched by your own body.

3 Hang downward for a few moments, then gently lift yourself back up, straightening your body but letting your head hang down. When your body is upright, lift your head back into its original position.

relaxation

In this exercise you should relax the muscles at the front of your body completely and then the muscles down your back. During the relaxation exercise, you need to feel and experience exactly how your body changes when it is in a relaxed state. Pay attention to the different sensations in your body, and how moving one part affects your whole body.

When you get to step 6 in the Relaxation exercise, you can slowly lift your body back up to step 3. Then, alternate the position of your feet and perform the rest of the sequence with your right leg forward.

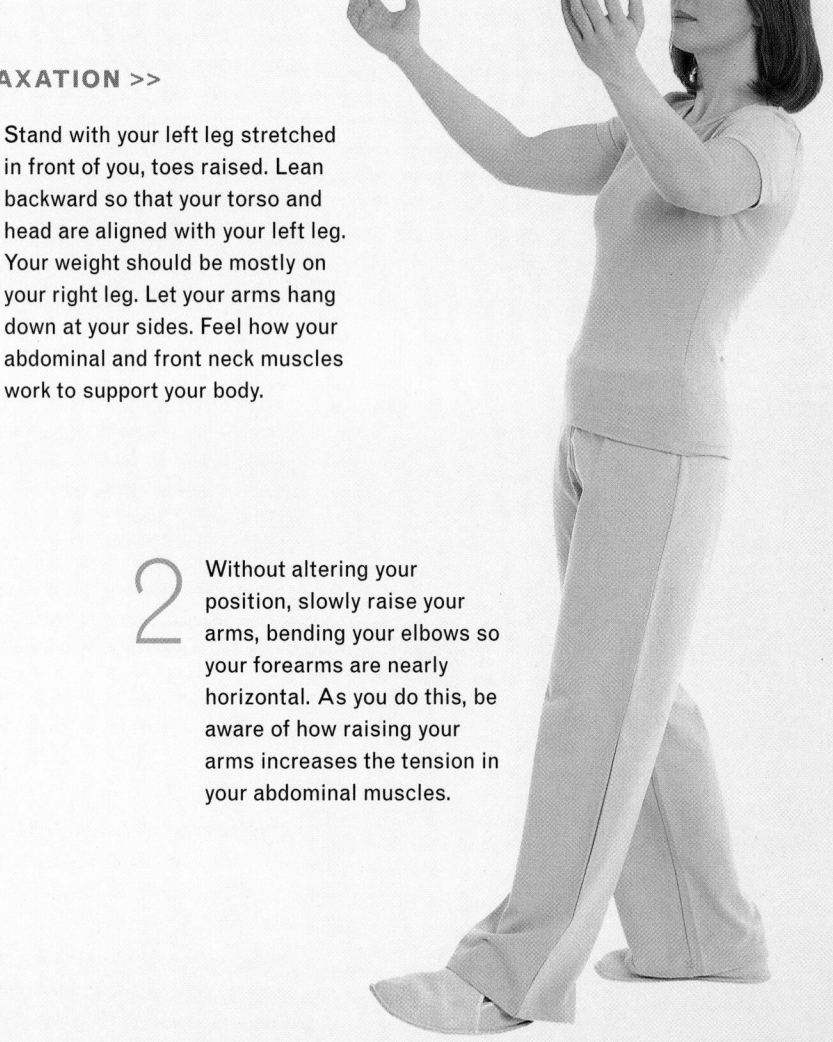

RELAXATION >>

1 Stand with your left leg stretched in front of you, toes raised. Lean backward so that your torso and head are aligned with your left leg. Your weight should be mostly on your right leg. Let your arms hang down at your sides. Feel how your abdominal and front neck muscles work to support your body.

2 Without altering your position, slowly raise your arms, bending your elbows so your forearms are nearly horizontal. As you do this, be aware of how raising your arms increases the tension in your abdominal muscles.

5 Continue to bend forward, using your back muscles rather than your abdominal muscles to support your body. Your elbows, wrists, and pectoral muscles should be relaxed. Keeping your palms the same distant apart, slide your hands down your leg without touching it.

6 Move your torso forward and shift your weight slowly onto your left foot, raising the heel of your right foot. Be careful not to lose your balance. Let your arms and head hang downward. Although you may habitually tense your neck when keeping your balance, you need to train yourself to relax your neck in this position.

4 Relax your arms, beginning at your wrists. Lower your chin, allowing your neck muscles to loosen. You should be using the muscles at the back of your body to support your head, rather than the muscles in the front of your body.

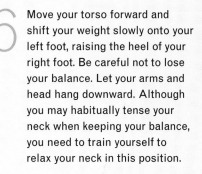

RELAXATION >>

3 Lift your arms as high as you can without straining. Try to relax your back muscles as much as possible, so that your abdominal muscles are supporting your body.

folding wings

This exercise uses the "beak" position in Single Whip of the t'ai chi Form (see page 50). You will stretch and loosen the muscles in your feet during this sequence. It also exercises the joints on either side of your groin, known as the inguinal crease or *kua* in Chinese (see page 68 for more information).

Balance plays a crucial role in this exercise, so it is useful to practice raising your heels off the ground several times to different heights while you are standing. This will accustom you to balancing using different parts of your feet.

FOLDING WINGS >>

1 Put the fingers and thumbs of both your hands together, forming a "beak." Lift your arms straight above your head and let your chest rise and expand. Raise your heels off the ground.

2 Open your arms wide apart with your hands out to your sides, palms facing downward.

FOLDING WINGS >>

3 Gradually lower your heels and begin to bend your knees. Keeping your back straight, lean forward while slowly lowering your arms.

6 Continue pushing your hands behind you while you bend your knees and lean forward. Extend your wrists as you complete this movement.

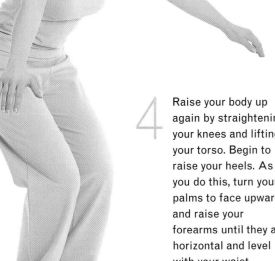

4 Raise your body up again by straightening your knees and lifting your torso. Begin to raise your heels. As you do this, turn your palms to face upward and raise your forearms until they are horizontal and level with your waist.

5 Keep raising your heels as you turn your palms over, lifting your elbows up to the sides of your body. Begin pushing backward with your palms.

"Study the uses of each posture with perseverance,
And you will find it is not difficult to attain.
If you pay attention to the region of the waist
So that the abdomen may relax
Then the chi will rise."

From "Song of the Thirteen Postures"

Take your time learning the Form. You should see the Form as a framework upon which you can build your performance of t'ai chi. Like any framework, it can serve as the basis for a variety of interpretations. Also, the more slowly you work through the Form, the more you will understand it and benefit from it.

3

>> the t'ai chi form

preparation, beginning

Start the Form with Preparation (see step 1, below). In Chinese culture it is believed that the south brings warmth, good luck, and Yang energy, so it is customary to face this direction when beginning the practice. The front of the body is Yin in nature and it needs the complement of Yang energy to strengthen it. The back of the body is Yang in nature, so it takes in the softer Yin energy from the north as its complement.

When raising your arms during the Beginning (see steps 2 and 3, below), you should feel your chest opening up, letting air flow into your lungs. Relax and breathe naturally. By the end of this movement you should feel your weight evenly distributed between both feet. Keep your spine and head aligned in a relaxed manner.

◆ **Visualization**
When you are standing still, imagine your head is lightly suspended from above, as if by a single hair.

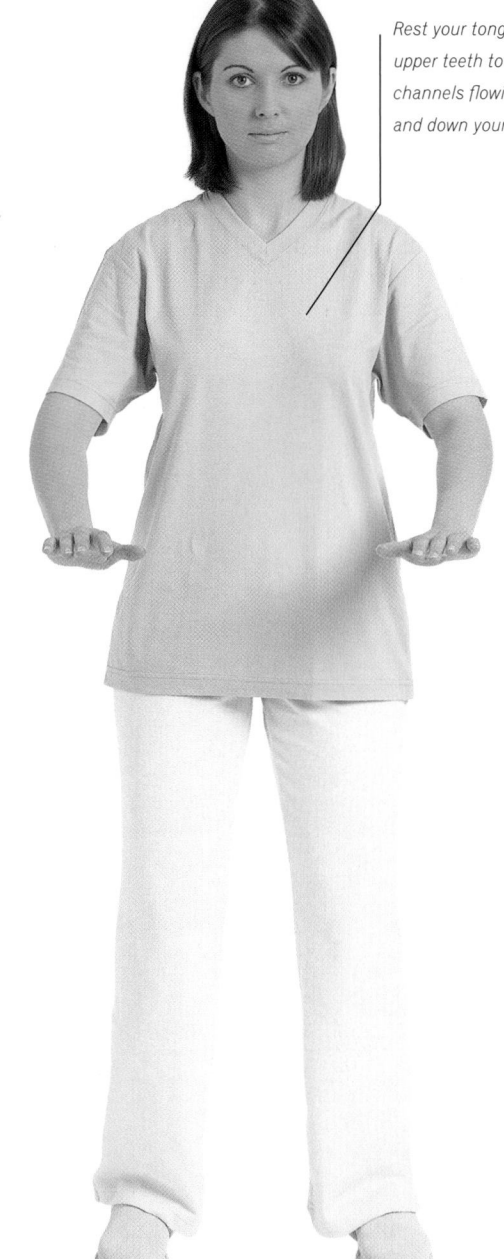

Rest your tongue behind your upper teeth to connect the chi channels flowing up your back and down your front.

POSTURE AND PACE

During the Beginning movement (steps 2 and 3) when you are lifting your arms, try not to lift your shoulders. This is a habit that causes tension throughout the body. T'ai chi movements like this can help to reduce such tendencies.

This opening movement sets the tone of what is to follow. In Beginning you decide the speed with which you will move for the rest of the Form. When practicing Beginning, you should remind yourself to move continuously at the same rate until you finish.

PREPARATION

1 Stand with your heels close together, toes pointing outward. Let your arms hang naturally. Remain in this position for a few seconds, as you calm yourself and focus on your practice.

BEGINNING >>

2 Step to the left with your left foot and turn it in so your toes point forward. Then turn your right foot in, pivoting on your heel, bringing both feet parallel. Begin raising your arms, keeping your hands horizontal.

3 Raise both your arms up in front of you until they are level with your collarbones, keeping your elbows slightly bent.

4 Bring your elbows down while slowly lowering your hands. They should come to rest level with your hips and remain horizontal.

hold a ball

Although it is not strictly a t'ai chi posture, the particular positioning of the hands in "Hold a Ball" occurs many times in t'ai chi sequences. It is a simplified version of the real movement. You never really position your hands as if holding an actual ball in the sequence: your hands pass by one another, making a specific movement that is difficult for most beginners to absorb. Instead of trying to describe this difficult movement—and frustrating new students—a teacher will ask them to perform "Hold a Ball." "Hold a Ball" is close enough to what the student does in the more complicated move for learning purposes.

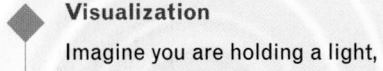

Visualization
Imagine you are holding a light, firm sphere, about the size of a beach ball, and moving it from one side of your body to the other.

Bend your knees slightly to avoid pressure on the joints.

CONFIDENCE BUILDER

"Hold a Ball" is used throughout Part Wild Horse's Mane (see page 28) and many other parts of the Form. Practicing the "Hold a Ball" movement can help you to understand how, in t'ai chi, your waist generates power that is spread throughout your body.

Flow from page 25

HOLD A BALL — RIGHT >>

1 Raise your left hand to chest-height and lower your right to hip-height as you turn your waist to the left.

2 Turn your waist back to the right while raising your right arm so it is opposite the right side of your chest, with your palm facing downward. Lower your left arm to hip-height and begin to move it underneath your right arm.

PART WILD HORSE'S MANE — LEFT >>

3 Bring your left foot, heel raised, closer to your right. Move your left hand beneath your right, with the palm up, as though you are holding a beach ball on your right side. Look at your right hand.

4 Keep your weight mainly on your right foot. Pivot on the ball of your left foot, turning your body 90 degrees to the left. You should look, and have your left foot pointing, to the left.

5 Step diagonally left and forward with your left foot, straightening out your right leg. Raise your left arm, until it is level with the top of your breast bone. As you raise your left hand, press your right down to the level of your left hip. Your left palm remains upward. You are now in the position which is known as the "Bow Stance."

part wild horse's mane — right

When your arms and hands pass one another during this movement, be aware of the sensation of their closeness and then of their separation. This will increase your sensitivity to the flow of chi. Part Wild Horse's Mane is good for your lungs, opening up your chest and improving breathing.

Don't concentrate on moving your arms. Let them follow your body.

◆ **Visualization**
During step 3, imagine your right hand is smoothing out a horse's mane, from the bottom of its neck up to its head.

FRONT HAND VARIATION

Another way to perform this movement is to change the positioning of your front hand, so that it is held with your palm facing your body. Whichever way you place your hand, make sure it is in the center of your body, in line with your chin, and that you are looking over the top of it. Your lower hand is in the same position in all versions of this movement. Your fingers should be pointing forward and there should be a gap of a few inches between your lower hand and your thigh.

If you experiment with any of these variations, notice how they change the overall feeling of the sequence and how they affect the rest of your body.

Flow from page 27

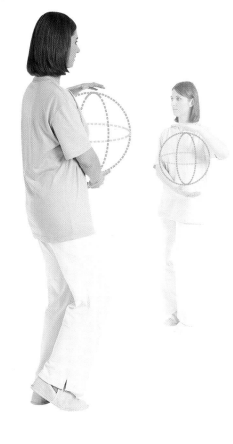

PART WILD HORSE'S MANE — RIGHT >>

1 Shift your weight back onto your right leg. Raise the toes of your left foot and turn it diagonally left, using your heel as a pivot. Turn both of your palms inward.

2 Move your weight onto your left foot. Lift your right heel and step forward with it, so your feet are together. At the same time, bring your arms to your left side to the "Hold a Ball" position with your left hand on top.

3 Make the "Bow Stance" by stepping diagonally forward with your right foot. As you do this, extend your right arm in front of you until it is level with the top of your breastbone. Your right palm remains facing upward, open at the Tiger's Mouth area (the space between the index finger and thumb). As your right hand rises, your left hand presses down to hip-height.

white crane spreads its wings

This movement is also known as Stork/Crane Cools Its Wings. The name may derive from one of the honorific titles given to the Taoist sages, "crane," indicating their status and longevity. Also, the Chinese character for "crane" contains the character for "cinnabar," the so-called elixir of life, said to be stored in the *dantien*.

In common with a number of t'ai chi movements, these positions involve one hand being in a low position, as if resting on something, which balances the raised right arm and stabilizes the body.

White Crane Spreads its Wings releases tension in the neck and shoulders, which improves both blood and chi circulation.

Visualization
Imagine your arms are the wings of a crane. They are fibrous and strong, yet pliable and light, helping you to balance and keep upright.

Let your arm lift your ribcage, expanding your lungs.

RAISED HAND VARIATION

The martial application of this move could be the deflection of a blow to your head using your right hand. However, a common variation of White Crane involves your right palm turned more inward and facing slightly downward, so that a line drawn from the center of your palm would meet a line drawn upward from between your legs. The forearm of your raised arm is then held further away from your upper body.

This variation was probably introduced into t'ai chi during the 1950s when it became part of the Chinese educational curriculum. In these newer Forms the aesthetic aspect is emphasized and the martial side is played down. While this variation may be more aesthetically pleasing, it lacks the effectiveness of the version shown on the left.

Flow from
page 29

PART WILD HORSE'S MANE — LEFT >>

1 Shift your weight back onto your left leg while raising your right toes. Turn your foot out to the right, using your heel as a pivot. Move your palms inward.

2 Turn your waist to the right, keeping your right toes raised. Move your right palm downward and your left upward. Bring both hands in front of you in the "Hold a Ball" position with your right hand on top.

3 Shift your weight onto your right foot and bring your left foot close to it, heel raised. Let your arms come in closer to your body.

WHITE CRANE SPREADS ITS WINGS >>

4 Step diagonally left into the "Bow Stance," your weight moving onto your left foot. Press down with your right palm so it is opposite your left hip and raise your left palm in front of you.

5 Slide your right foot forward a few inches closer to your left foot. As you do this, bring both hands in front of you into the "Hold a Ball" position, your left hand on top. Begin raising your left heel.

6 As your left heel is rising, settle your weight onto your right foot. At the same time, press down beside your left thigh with your left hand and raise your right hand, above your head, palm outward.

brush left knee and push

This movement is also known as Brush Knee and Twist Step. One of the Chinese characters for this sequence is a spiral shape, like that a silkworm spins during its metamorphosis. The performance of t'ai chi is traditionally compared to the smooth, delicate action required to "harvest" silk from a cocoon.

In this movement, your body twists first to the right (see step 2, below) and then back to the left (step 3). Energy is compressed in your feet by the first twist and spirals back through your legs, spine, and arms with the second. The first movement is what an athlete might call a "wind-up," and the second a release of that wound-up energy. The effect of this spiraling energy can be clearly felt once a practitioner is sufficiently sensitive and relaxed.

◆ **Visualization**
When you rotate your waist during step 3, try to visualize the spiraling energy (see above) as red light moving up your body. Doing this will help the energy to move more easily.

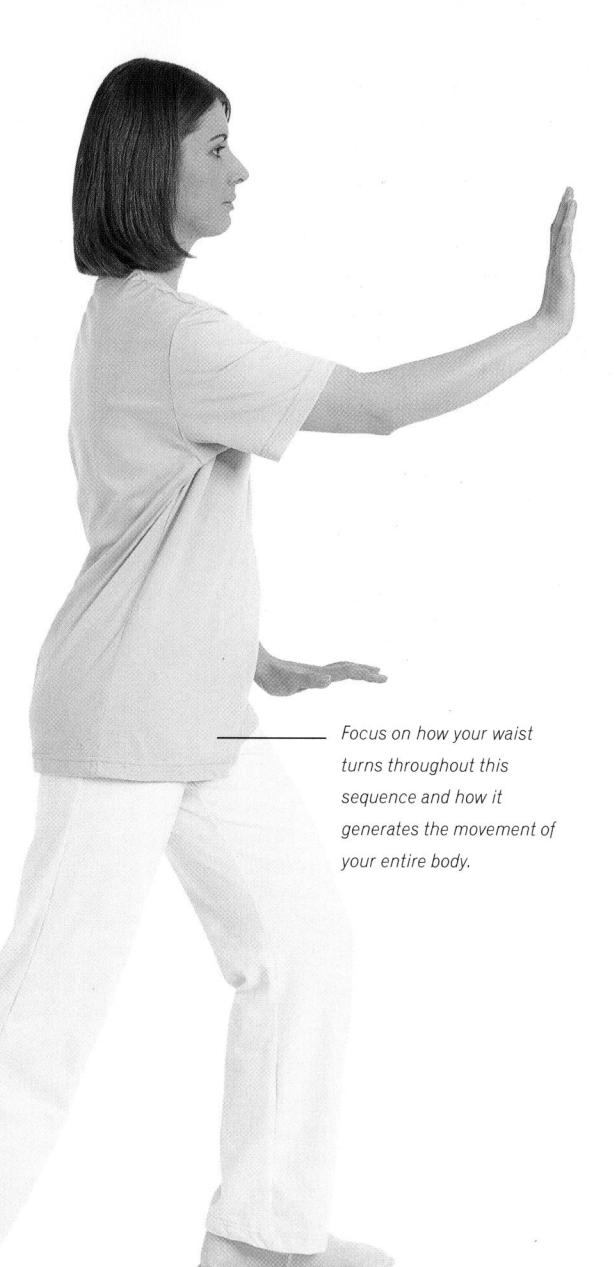

Focus on how your waist turns throughout this sequence and how it generates the movement of your entire body.

WRIST AND HAND VARIATIONS

Brush Knee and Push can vary in the angles of the pushing and brushing wrists, which can be wider than illustrated on page 33. Also, when you bring your right arm behind you, before brushing forward, the angle of your hand and wrist to your forearm can vary. According to the principles of Yin and Yang (see page 10), you should allow your wrist to bend and soften, before pushing ahead.

As you become more experienced, you will find your movements becoming more internal, and visibly subtler. However, if you are taking t'ai chi classes, your teacher may need to see subtle changes like these demonstrated to make sure you have understood the concept being taught. This is one reason for visual differences in how people perform the t'ai chi Form.

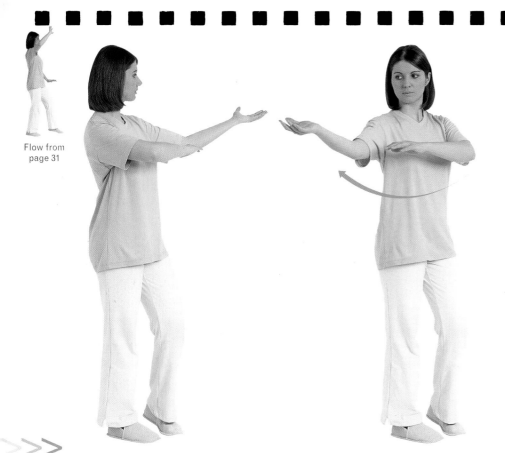

Flow from page 31

BRUSH LEFT KNEE AND PUSH >>

1 Bring your left foot, heel raised, beside your right foot. Bring your left hand up in front of you, extended but bent slightly at the elbow. Raise your right arm level to your left arm, with the right hand, palm down, pointing to your left elbow.

2 Turn right and look back over your right shoulder. In turning, raise your right hand level with your shoulder, palm facing upward, and lower your left hand, palm facing downward, so it is beside your right elbow. Look toward your right hand.

3 Shift your body to the left and step diagonally forward with your left foot into the "Bow Stance." As you step, press down with your left palm and bend your right elbow, so your right hand is level with your right shoulder. At the same time, rotate your right wrist so your fingers are pointing forward.

4 Shift your weight onto your left foot as you place it on the floor. At the same time, without touching your leg, "brush" in front of your left knee with your left hand bringing it up to hip-height. As you "brush" with your left hand, "push" straight forward with your right hand, keeping it level with your shoulder.

brush right knee and push

W hen you move into Brush Right Knee and Push from Brush Left Knee and Push, remind yourself that you often move backward first before taking a step forward in the Form. Many people learning t'ai chi are tempted to rush this backward weight-shift because it is unusual to do this when stepping forward, and because they are intent on progressing through the Form. It is important to take this movement slowly and give it your full attention, especially before you turn your body. Performing this weight-shift correctly enhances your stability and balance.

◆ **Visualization**
When performing this movement, think of your spine as the mainmast of a sailing ship and your arms as the sails.

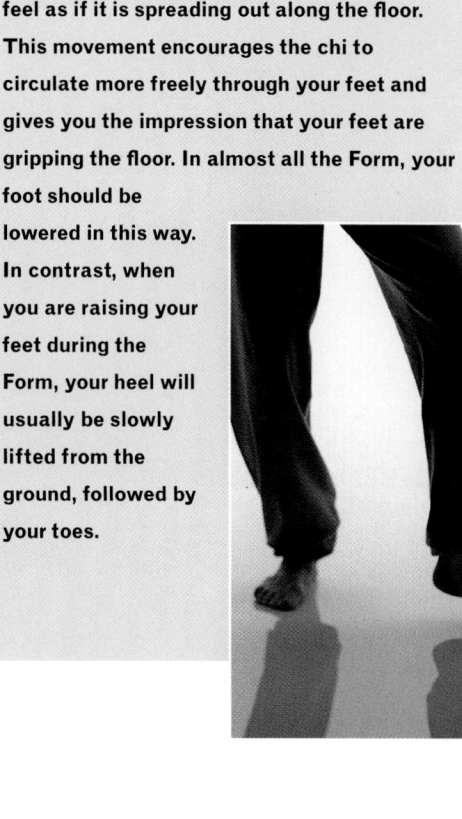

Look over the top of your left hand.

Don't strain your right knee by extending it further than your toes.

FOOT FOCUS

When you place your foot on the floor and unroll it forward from your heel, let your foot feel as if it is spreading out along the floor. This movement encourages the chi to circulate more freely through your feet and gives you the impression that your feet are gripping the floor. In almost all the Form, your foot should be lowered in this way. In contrast, when you are raising your feet during the Form, your heel will usually be slowly lifted from the ground, followed by your toes.

Flow from
page 33

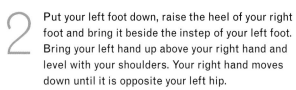

BRUSH RIGHT KNEE AND PUSH >>

1 Shift your weight back onto your right leg and turn your left foot diagonally to the left, raising the toes. As your weight shifts, start to raise your left hand, palm facing up, toward your left shoulder. Bring your right hand, palm facing down, in line with your left elbow. Look toward your left hand.

2 Put your left foot down, raise the heel of your right foot and bring it beside the instep of your left foot. Bring your left hand up above your right hand and level with your shoulders. Your right hand moves down until it is opposite your left hip.

3 Step diagonally forward with your right foot into the "Bow Stance." As you do this, move your right hand forward to "Brush" in front of your right knee and up to hip-height. At the same time, move your left palm forward to make a "Push," keeping your hand level with your shoulders. End this movement with most of your weight on your right leg.

brush left knee and push, play guitar

Sometimes called Strum the Lute, Play Guitar (steps 3 to 5 below) is performed with most of your weight on your right leg. This can initially be a strain for some students, so if it is, put some more weight on your left foot until your legs are stronger. If you imagine that your outstretched hands are holding a partner's arm at the wrist and elbow, you will have the correct positioning for your arms and hands. Your arms should be in line with each other, as if the arm you are gripping is straightened.

Since the sound of an acoustic guitar depends on the hollow interior of the instrument providing a place for the string to resonate, it has been suggested that when you practice t'ai chi, you become this hollow space in which the silent music of t'ai chi can resonate. Play Guitar reminds us of this.

◆ Visualization

As you raise your arms during this movement, imagine you are holding something soft, like an armful of leaves or feathers, then as you straighten your arms, imagine that it becomes something rounded and more solid.

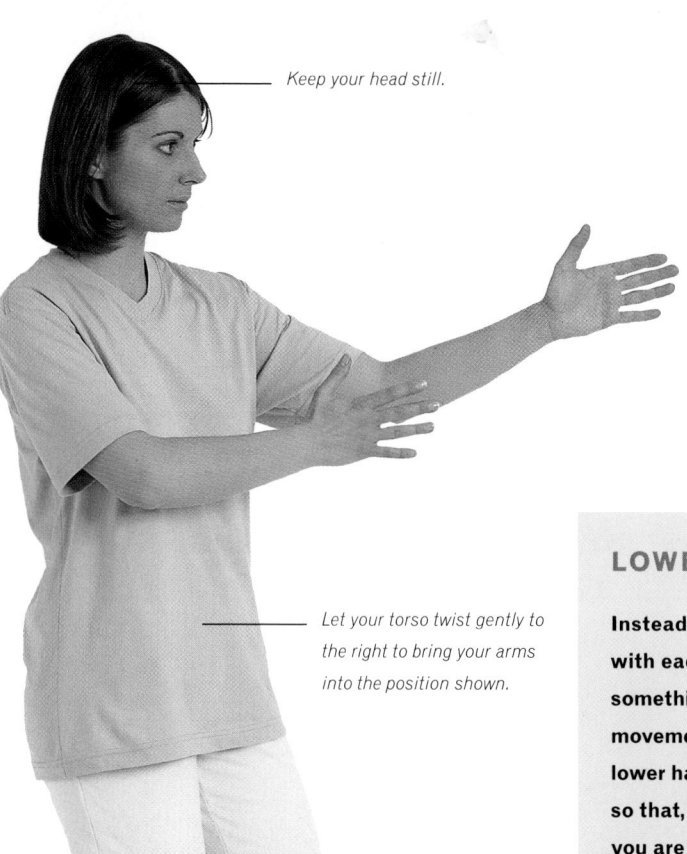

Keep your head still.

Let your torso twist gently to the right to bring your arms into the position shown.

LOWER ARM VARIATION

Instead of having your arms and hands in line with each other, as if you are gripping something straight, one variation of the movement is to hold the lower hand further down, so that, if you imagine you are holding an arm, the arm would be coming down almost vertically in front of you.

Flow from
page 35

BRUSH LEFT KNEE AND PUSH >>

1 Shift your weight back onto your left foot and turn your right foot out diagonally, raising your toes while turning your body to the right. As your weight shifts, extend your right hand up to chest-height, palm facing upward. Bring your left hand, palm facing down, across your body so you are pointing at your right elbow. Look toward your right palm.

2 Move into the "Bow Stance," stepping diagonally forward with your left foot and lowering your right toes. Move your left hand down to "Brush" in front of your left knee, then raise it up to hip-height. At the same time, "Push" forward with your right palm. This movement should end with most of your weight on your left leg.

PLAY GUITAR >>

3 Shift your weight onto your left foot and draw your right foot, with the heel raised, closer to it. As your weight shifts, move both hands in front of your body, with the palms downward.

4 Draw your weight back onto your right foot and raise your left heel from the floor as you bring your right elbow into your body, moving your left hand a hand's-width ahead of your right. Keep both of your arms horizontal, with the fingers pointing down 45 degrees. Look across the top of your left hand.

5 Push your left foot out, toes raised, and place it on the ground with your leg almost straight. Extend your arms forward, with your left hand at shoulder-height. Move your right hand to beside your left elbow. Keep both palms hollowed and your fingers pointing forward.

step back and drive monkey away — right

This movement is the only one in the Form where you step fully backward and end with your weight on your back foot. The name of this movement may be connected to a Chinese legend. The story tells of a duke who went hunting for monkeys on a mountain. All of the monkeys, except one, hid from him. This monkey showed off and even caught the duke's arrow when he shot at him. But eventually, with the help of his retainers, the duke killed the monkey. The duke reflected that it was the monkey's desire to show off his skill that had led to its death. The duke's companion, Yen Pui, took this lesson to heart and from then on dispensed with everything that made him stand out, driving away the boastful nature of the monkey.

The twisting action of the waist during this movement is of benefit to the kidneys. For information on how to enhance this, try the visualization below.

From a horizontal position, raise your palm to be almost vertical as you push forward.

MARTIAL APPLICATION

This sequence can also be used as a self-defense move. You can imagine the following sequence as you perform this movement. First, a partner seizes hold of your front arm at the wrist. You step back, turning your front arm around, from Yang to Yin. This produces a twisting action. Your stepping back makes your partner step forward, his or her arm being twisted, and then your rear arm comes through, rests on his or her arm, and pushes. The combined pull, twist, and push breaks your partner's grip.

◆ **Visualization**

Focus on your kidney region for this movement, around the small of your back. Pay particular attention as you twist in the beginning, when the use of your waist and the movement around the kidneys is more obvious.

Flow from
page 37

STEP BACK AND DRIVE MONKEY AWAY — RIGHT >>

1 Lower your right hand down to your thigh, then raise it up behind you, palm upward, until it is level with your shoulder. Stretch your left hand forward, palm facing down. Your feet stay more or less in place, and your body begins to turn to the right. As you turn, look at your right palm.

2 Look forward, bend your right elbow, and bring your right hand close to your ear, palm facing downward. Turn your left hand over and begin moving your arm downward. Begin stepping backward with your left foot, with your heel raised.

3 Straighten your right leg as you step backward with your left foot. Push ahead with your right hand, palm almost vertical, and pull your left palm in beside your left thigh. As you complete the movement, pivot on the ball of your right foot and turn your heel out to the right, so that your foot points forward. Rest your weight on your left leg.

step back and drive monkey away — left

This position has particular health benefits connected with acupuncture/chi kung points. The *ming-men* or "Gate of Life" acupuncture/chi kung point is opposite the navel, on the spine (see page 11 for more information). Beside it are two kidney points, and running along the muscles of the spine on either side of the vertebral column are important channels, such as the bladder. When performed correctly, Step Back and Drive Monkey Away benefits the *ming-men* point, which is opened up by the movement. This relieves any congestion in the point caused by bad posture, for example, and lets the chi flow through. The twisting action of the move stimulates both the bladder and kidneys.

Visualization

When you turn your arms over from Yang (palm facing up) to Yin (palm facing down), synchronize your wrist movements. Concentrating on simple actions like these improves your overall performance of the whole t'ai chi Form.

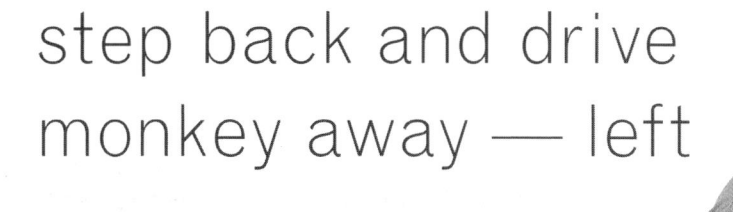

At the end of this movement, don't completely extend your left elbow so it locks. Keep your arm slightly bent.

HAND AND KNEE VARIATIONS

Instead of pushing their rear hands to the front in a straight line, level with shoulder-height (see left), some practitioners of Step Back and Drive Monkey Away bring their hands down to the height of their solar plexus, past their shoulders, and then back up to chin-height (see right). Varying your movements will depend on your experience, flexibility, and balance. The more you practice t'ai chi, the more subtle and intricate your movements will become.

The depth of your knee bend will vary so that, through practice, your knees will become strong enough for you to place most of your weight on your rear leg.

Flow from
page 39

STEP BACK AND DRIVE MONKEY AWAY — LEFT >>

1 Raise your left arm diagonally behind you with your palm up. Look at it as it moves. Relax your right arm to a straightened position, with your palm down. Turn your body to the left, moving smoothly and naturally.

2 As you take this step, turn both palms over at the same time. Bend your left elbow and bring your hand forward and level to your shoulder, palm facing down. As you do this, draw your right hand, palm up, toward your right leg. At the same time, lift the heel of your right foot and begin to step backward with it.

3 Push your left hand forward, palm almost vertical. Place your right foot behind you and move your weight onto it as you straighten your left leg. Turn your left heel to the left, pivoting on the ball of your foot so your toes point forward.

Repeat Step Back and Drive Monkey Away — Right, page 39, and Step Back and Drive Monkey Away — Left.

hold a ball and ward off — left

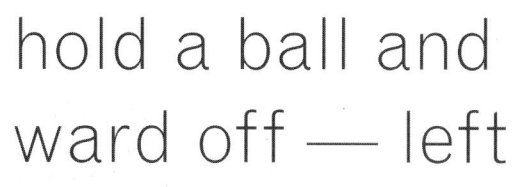

Ward Off is a defensive movement, as described in the section on Push Hands (see page 90). It demonstrates the t'ai chi theory that moving in a straight line toward an oncoming movement will result in a destructive collision, whereas a curved movement (here, the shielding posture of the left arm) can take in, and roll with, the oncoming force. It is also one of the principal postures for training one's arms to become responsive to the different pressures a partner exerts.

Ward Off and its following movements—Roll Back, Press, and Push—are known collectively as Grasp the Bird's Tail. They are considered the fundamental moves of t'ai chi. The name comes from the image of examining a small bird, holding it carefully and inspecting it attentively. Use the same mindfulness and close attention when you are performing these movements.

◆ **Visualization**
Imagine yourself centered yet flexible during Ward Off, blending with and redirecting the energy of an attack.

STANCE AND ARM VARIATIONS

Depth of stance is the most common variation with this movement. As your legs become stronger, you can step further forward in making the "Bow Stance." The energy and circulation of blood in the legs and hips provide you with a sense of rootedness, less caught up in the whirl of thoughts and emotions in your upper body.

A less common variation is to keep your left arm (or right arm in Ward Off— Right) more open and further forward, so that you would not be able to hold a ball against your chest, as shown right.

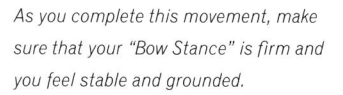

— As you complete this movement, make sure that your "Bow Stance" is firm and you feel stable and grounded.

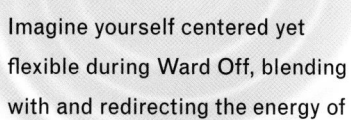
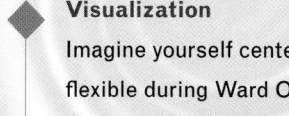

Flow from page 41

HOLD A BALL AND WARD OFF — LEFT >>

1 Turn to your right, bringing your left foot back, heel raised, beside your right foot. Raise your right hand, palm down, to the middle of your chest. Bring your left hand down, palm facing up, under your right hand, to the "Hold a Ball" position. Look at your right hand.

2 Move your left foot forward diagonally, lower your heel to the ground, and shift your weight onto it, straightening your right leg. At the same time, raise your left arm in front of your body, palm facing in, as if holding a beach ball to your chest. Press downward with your right palm opposite your left thigh.

ROLL BACK >>

3 Turn your body a little to the left and turn your left hand away from your body. Do not turn your arm, your body should be moving as a whole. As you turn left, your right arm rises with the elbow bent and the palm up, beside your left elbow. Look over the top of your left hand.

4 Shift your body to the right, moving your weight onto your right foot and straightening your left leg. Raise your right arm up and across to the right until it is level with your shoulders and pointing away from your body. Move your left arm across your body at chest-height so you are pointing to your right elbow. Look to your right.

press, push

The original calligraphic symbol of Press looked like a hand touching ears of corn, an image suggesting harmony. Now, the character is normally associated with more stressful situations, such as elbowing one's way into a bus or elevator. We can combine both the ancient and modern-day contexts in a martial application by performing Press with some assertive Yang force to connect and then harmonize with a partner.

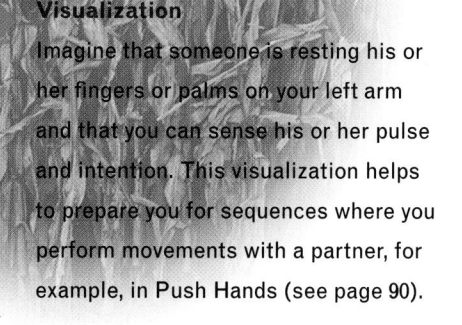

Visualization

Imagine that someone is resting his or her fingers or palms on your left arm and that you can sense his or her pulse and intention. This visualization helps to prepare you for sequences where you perform movements with a partner, for example, in Push Hands (see page 90).

Bending your right wrist during Press can cut off or reduce the flow of chi, so take care to keep your wrist flat.

HAND VARIATION

The hands are usually placed in the position shown in the picture on the left, or something very close to it. In old drawings and photographs of the modern promoter of the style, Yang Cheng-fu, he is shown resting his rear palm on his left forearm. In the method shown in the Form we are following, though, the fingertips are touching the pulse region.

Flow from page 43

PRESS >>

1 Face front and bring the fingertips of your right hand to touch the inside of your left wrist, which is facing your chest. You should look at your hand as your fingertips rest very lightly on your wrist, as if taking your pulse.

2 Shift your body weight forward onto your left foot and begin pushing your arms out, fingertips still in place. Extend your right leg, lift your head, and look forward.

PUSH >>

3 Straighten your arms and turn your left palm downward while slipping the fingers of your right hand across the back of your left hand, as if you are washing it. At the same time, shift your weight back onto your right foot.

4 Bring both hands close to your chest, dropping your elbows down and keeping your hands horizontal, palms down.

5 Shift your weight onto your front foot while pushing your hands down and forward, then up and forward. Finish with your palms vertical and facing out in front of you.

hold a ball and ward off — right, roll back

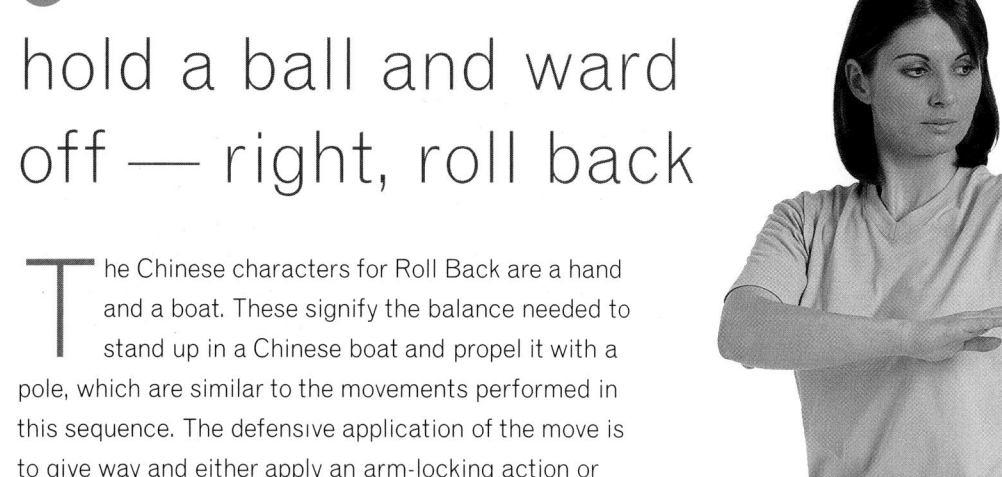

Keep your arms light and free.

The Chinese characters for Roll Back are a hand and a boat. These signify the balance needed to stand up in a Chinese boat and propel it with a pole, which are similar to the movements performed in this sequence. The defensive application of the move is to give way and either apply an arm-locking action or guide force away from oneself without resisting it directly. It is the second movement in the Grasp the Bird's Tail group of sequences (see page 42), and flows very naturally from Ward Off. Beginners often make the mistake of not completing Ward Off (steps 1–3) before beginning Roll Back (steps 4–5), so remember to move carefully through this sequence. Roll Back is beneficial for your abdominal muscles, as the sweeping movement of your arms stretches and strengthens them.

MARTIAL ART VARIATION

The armlocking technique is applied by turning (steps 4 to 5, below) while your right arm presses against an opponent's elbow joint as your other hand holds his wrist. A well–known variation is shown below, where your right arm stays bent and moves horizontally across your chest. This version is more efficient as an armlock, but it is less smooth and beneficial (in terms of chi and flexibility) than the type practiced in this Form.

◆ **Visualization**

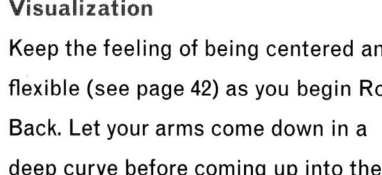

Keep the feeling of being centered and flexible (see page 42) as you begin Roll Back. Let your arms come down in a deep curve before coming up into the position shown right.

Flow from page 45

HOLD A BALL AND WARD OFF — RIGHT >>

1 Turn your body to the right, shifting most of your weight onto your right foot. "Wipe" your hands horizontally to the right, out across your chest.

2 Bring your weight onto your left foot and bring your right foot, heel up, close to your left foot. Turn your body to the left as you bring your hands back to the left side of your body to the "Hold a Ball" position, left hand on top.

3 Step diagonally right with your right foot into the "Bow Stance" while raising your right arm in front of your body, palm facing in, as if you were holding a beach ball to your chest. With your left palm press downward opposite your right thigh.

ROLL BACK >>

4 Turn your body slightly to the right, moving your right hand away from your body and raising it to head-height. At the same time bring your left hand, palm up, to beside your right elbow. Look over the top of your right hand.

5 Shift your body to the left, moving your weight onto your left foot. Gently swing your left arm down, then out to the left side of your body, elbow slightly bent. At the same time, lower your right hand down to your right thigh, then raise it in front of you, so you point toward the wrist of your left hand.

press, push, repeat

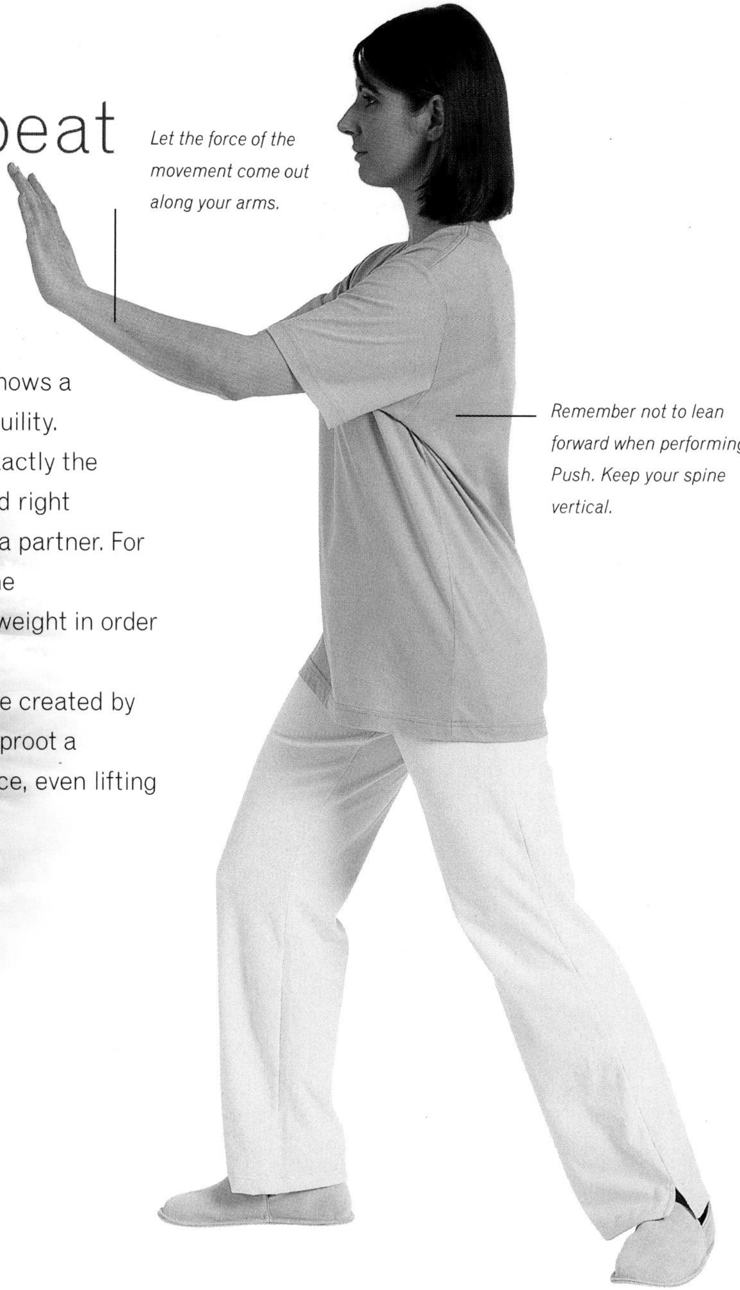

Let the force of the movement come out along your arms.

Push, the last movement in the group known as Grasp the Bird's Tail (see page 42), contains the Chinese characters for "hand" in its name, as do the other three movements. The other character shows a woman under a roof, implying peace and tranquility. "Push" is a movement that uses the hand in exactly the right way: with right direction, right energy, and right intention. This is important in sequences with a partner. For example, Push Hands (see page 90) requires the development of sensitivity to a partner's body weight in order to be performed correctly.

In terms of its martial application, the shape created by Push, of a "wave crashing on the shore," can uproot a partner or opponent by causing a loss of balance, even lifting him or her clear off the ground.

Remember not to lean forward when performing Push. Keep your spine vertical.

◆ **Visualization**
As you push forward, feel that a space is opening up in front of you and that any difficulties or obstructions that you may be experiencing in your life are moving easily out of your way.

STRAIGHT PUSH VARIATION

This movement's one major variation concerns the trajectory of the push. In the Form shown in this book, beginning from the position in which the hands are held in front of the chest (see step 1, below), the hands move downward in a curve to about waist-level, and then rise back up to chest-level. Some practitioners of t'ai chi use a different movement. They simply push forward in a straight line. However, the wave-like movement in the Form shown here is more martially effective than a simple push in a straight line.

Flow from page 47

Flow from
page 47

PRESS >>

1 Turn your body to the right, bringing the fingertips of your left hand to touch your right wrist, which is facing your chest. Your fingertips rest lightly on your wrist, as if taking your pulse.

2 Shift your weight forward onto your right foot, and push your arms out almost straight, fingertips still in place.

PUSH >>

3 Turn your right palm downward, at the same time slipping the fingers of your left hand across the back of your right hand, as if you are washing it. Begin to shift your weight backward.

4 Bring both hands close to your chest, facing away from you, as you shift your weight to your left foot.

5 Move your weight to your right foot and push your hands down and forward, then up and forward.

single whip

This is the only movement you will not find in other martial arts systems. The liver benefits, since the surrounding area is opened and stretched by the movement.

As you begin to perform Single Whip, your arms and hands move separately. Your right arm moves away with your hand in the "beak" position (see step 2, below), like the end of a whip being straightened, followed by your left, open, flat hand, as if it is the handle of the whip. Both arms create the shape of an extended whip (see step 5).

◆ **Visualization**
Imagine that your arms are a whip as you perform this movement. Try to feel the fluid connection they have with each other and the way your body's energy flows across them.

Remember to move from your dantien, keeping your shoulders and arms relaxed.

Put your fingers and thumb together to create the "beak."

LATER WU VARIATION

Shown here is the final position of Single Whip from a style of t'ai chi called the Later Wu Style. The student is facing the front, his arms are equally placed on either side of his body, and his weight and balance are centralized. This is a very open position: both arms and legs are extended away from the trunk, and the angles made by the limbs to the body are wide.

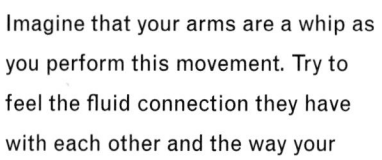

Flow from page 49

Flow from page 49

SINGLE WHIP >>

1 Step forward and slightly left, shifting your weight onto your left foot. "Wipe" your hands to the left across your body at chest-height.

2 Transfer your weight onto your right foot, raise your left heel, and move your left foot closer to your right foot. Make the "Hold a Ball" position on your right side, with your right hand forming a "beak" shape, and your four fingertips meeting the tip of your thumb.

3 Step forward and left slightly with the heel of your left foot, ready for the "Bow Stance." Straighten your right arm, moving the "beak" right hand outward diagonally in line with your right shoulder. Look at your right hand.

4 Lower your left foot into the "Bow Stance" and turn your waist around to the left. At the same time, lift your left hand upward, and then push it away and in front of you until is level with your face, with the palm away from you.

wave hands in clouds — left

This movement is also known as Cloud Hands, Cloud Built Hands, and Wave Hands Like Clouds. With this movement, try to feel during steps 1–2, below, as if your hands are invisibly connected, so that as your higher (right) hand is crossing your chest it draws your lower hand behind it and across your abdomen. During steps 3–5, as the positions of your arms change over, feel that their roles change too, and now your left hand is higher and towing your right.

◆ Visualization
Imagine how clouds are formed from vapor rising and condensing as you move your arms. Clouds are light, beautiful, and cotton-like. When "pushed" by the wind they move with little or no resistance.

Keep your gaze on your hands throughout this sequence.

CHI FOCUS

Remember that the flow of chi energy is very important in t'ai chi. The variation of Wave Hands in Clouds shown below clearly indicates the movement of chi. (This is because the movement of hands can "direct" chi through the body.) The hands are facing the body and are in a vertical line with one another. This means that the *lao-gong* points of the hands (see page 11), where chi can be focused, also face the body and can exchange chi with it or influence the chi passing through it. Experiment with the variation of step 3, shown right, to see how it alters the overall feeling of the movement.

Flow from page 51

WAVE HANDS IN CLOUDS — LEFT >>

1 Pivot right on your left heel, shifting weight onto your right foot. Open your right hand and bring your left hand, facing inward, down in front of your left thigh.

2 Begin shifting your weight onto your left foot. Turn and look right as you bring your right arm to the right, with your palm down. Let your left arm move across your body above your right hip.

3 Shift more of your weight onto your left foot, raise your left hand to the "Hold a Ball" position and lower your right hand to waist-height.

4 Turn your waist and torso to the left and let both your arms move to the left side of your body. There should be no other movements with your arms.

5 Draw your right foot back parallel with your left. Your weight moves over to your left side as your hands continue moving left.

wave hands in clouds — right

In general, the Chinese regard the heart as an organ where we never intentionally try to focus chi. So as you perform Wave Hands, keep your high hand more or less above your heart. Do not draw your hand right across your heart, as this will direct the flow of chi toward it.

This movement can also be practiced sitting down, which is useful way to train—the fact that you are static on the seat prevents your hips from moving and emphasizes the muscles used to turn your waist.

◆ **Visualization**
T'ai chi is sometimes described as meditation in motion. Remain as mindful as possible of how your body is moving and feeling. If your thoughts start to wander, gently bring them back to your body.

As you move your torso, do not tense up your shoulders or arms.

MARTIAL APPLICATION

Wave Hands can be used defensively or offensively in a combat situation. Both hands during steps 3 and 4 might be sweeping aside attacks to the upper and lower body, or they could both be attacking the same areas of an opponent.

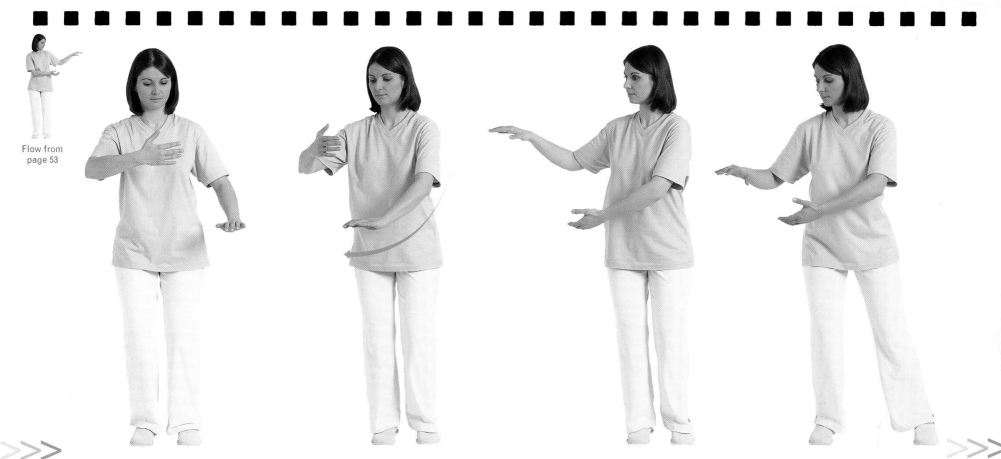

Flow from page 53

WAVE HANDS IN CLOUDS — RIGHT >>

1 Turn your body to face front, raising your right hand to chest-height, with your palm facing you, and lower your left hand to hip-height.

2 Begin moving your left hand underneath your right, into the "Hold a Ball" position. Start to turn your torso to the right.

3 Turn your torso a little more to the right, letting your arms move with it.

4 Keep moving your torso and arms to the right. Step out with your left foot, and begin to move your weight onto it.

sink the shoulders

There are a number of basic principles in t'ai chi to observe when practicing the Form. Central to the Yang style are the Ten Essentials—the basic principles of t'ai chi that apply throughout the entire Form—written by Yang Cheng-fu. Principles one to five are as follows. Principles six to ten are described on page 58.

Sink the shoulders and elbows **to insure a flow of energy is established from the feet, through the spine, along the arms, and into the hands. Raising the shoulders and elbows creates blockages that can impede the flow of energy through the body.**

Hollow the chest **to help release tension from the upper body and allow the chi to settle in the** *dantien***.**

Relax the waist **encouraging a more efficient use of the body and releasing tension from the upper body and chest. Releasing this tension will improve your performance of t'ai chi.**

Staying relaxed in the shoulders is crucial to performing the Waves Hands in Clouds sequence correctly.

REMEMBER:

• **Sink the shoulders and elbows**

• **Hollow the chest**

• **Relax the waist**

• **Distinguish between substantial and insubstantial foot positions**

• **Apply the mind rather than muscular force**

Distinguish between substantial and insubstantial foot positions **because in most postures, the weight is distributed 70 percent on one leg (substantial) and 30 percent on the other (insubstantial). Recognize the points at which weight is transferred from one foot to the other.**

Apply the mind rather than muscular force **so when performing movements, the mind (***yi***) should be used rather than muscular force. Visualizing the application of the movement with the mind is more effective than just using physical strength.**

Flow from page 55

WAVE HANDS IN CLOUDS — LEFT REPEAT >>

1 Turn your torso to the left so you are facing front. Begin placing your hands into the "Hold a Ball" position, raising your left hand to chest-height and lowering your right hand to hip-height.

2 Continue turning your torso to the left, letting your left hand move out away from your body while your right hand moves across your hips. At the same time, keep your weight moving onto your left leg, which should be slightly bent.

3 As your weight shifts, straighten your left arm so it is facing away from you and parallel with the side of your body. Keep your elbow slightly bent and your palm facing downward.

4 Bring your right foot closer to your left, so your feet are parallel. Let your arms come closer together and let your weight move to your left.

keep the head erect

Principles six through ten of the Ten Essentials written by Yang Cheng-fu are as follows. (Principles one to five are described on page 56.) By maintaining these principles, you will find that your practice of the Form becomes easier.

Keeping your head erect during Wave Hands in Clouds allows your shoulders to move freely.

Keep the head erect by imagining that it is suspended from above. With the head suspended, the body forms a straight line for the energy to rise from the base of the spine to the crown of the head. A bowed head interrupts the flow of energy.

Coordinate the upper and lower body so it moves as a whole, with a connection between the upper and lower torso. Movements originate from the waist and everything else follows as one connected unit.

Coordinate the inner and outer parts so every movement comes from the connection between mind and body. The mind determines the direction and the body moves with it. Imagining the position that your body should be in can be considered an "inner" posture. If you can harmonize the inner and outer postures, you will achieve the optimal result. T'ai chi relaxes the mind and body, strengthens muscles, and enhances wellbeing.

REMEMBER:

• **Keep the head erect**

• **Coordinate the upper and lower body**

• **Coordinate the inner and outer parts**

• **Continuous and flowing movements**

• **Inner tranquility and peace in movement**

Continuous and flowing movements are necessary for t'ai chi. Your Form should always be smooth, even, and performed in a continuous, flowing way.

Inner tranquility and peace in movement as illustrated by the expression "Move like a river, be still as a mountain." This describes the fluid yet grounded type of movement we are aiming for when performing the postures.

Flow from page 57

Flow from page 57

WAVE HANDS IN CLOUDS — RIGHT REPEAT >>

1 Lift your right hand to chest-height, palm facing toward you. Rotate your left forearm into your body, palm down.

2 As you perform Wave Hands, keep your gaze in the direction of the higher of your two hands. Start shifting your weight back onto your right foot, and begin carrying the "ball" to the right side of your body.

3 Turn your torso slightly to the right, letting your arms move with it. Let your gaze follow your arms as they move to the right. Continue moving your weight onto your right foot.

4 Continue moving your torso and arms to the right. Step out to the left with your left foot, and begin to move your weight onto it.

5 As you shift your weight, lift your left hand, palm facing inward, to shoulder-height. Lower your right hand, palm facing downward, to hip-height.

high pat on horse

This sequence is sometimes called Step Up to Examine Horse, which is a more accurate translation of the Chinese characters. The characters imply an examination of something high and noble. You should perform High Pat on Horse in a gentle, exploratory way, a mind-set expressed with your hands but felt in the whole of your body.

This is one of the few movements in the Form where most of your weight stays on one leg—the right one in this case. Use this as an opportunity to improve your sense of balance and strengthen your leg muscles.

◆ **Visualization**

As your left hand turns over (see step 5 below), imagine it is cupping a horse's jaw. Then, as you bring your right hand forward, imagine that you are placing it on the forehead of the horse and gently stroking it.

Put very little weight on your left leg.

EXPERIENCING CHI

Be aware of the Yang (upward-facing) and Yin (downward-facing) positions of your hands during High Pat on Horse. Your palms should pass one another in front of your chest, and you should try to perceive the chi energy moving between them.

Flow from page 59

SINGLE WHIP >>

1 Turn your body slightly to the right. Bring your left hand opposite your right hip and bring your right arm up, bending it at the elbow so your right hand is at chest-height and above your left hand. Form a "beak" with your right hand by bringing your fingers and thumb together.

2 Raise your left heel and turn your foot 45 degrees to the left. At the same time, straighten your right arm away from your body, keeping your "beak" hand at shoulder-height.

3 Step diagonally left, straightening your right leg, and turn your torso to the left so you are in the "Bow Stance." Push directly ahead of you with your left hand, palm facing away from you. Look straight ahead.

HIGH PAT ON HORSE >>

4 Begin to draw back your left foot, raising your heel. Move your right arm further to the right and open your hand up, with the palm upward. Turn your left palm so it faces downward. Look over at your right hand.

5 Turn your head back to the left so you are looking ahead of you. Move your right arm out across your body so that it is almost straight, palm facing down. Move your left hand down to your left hip, palm up.

separate right foot

This movement is sometimes translated as Kick with Right Foot. However, the Chinese characters for the name contain the idea of separating rather than a violent kick. Simply stretch your right leg out, point your toes, and notice the benefits of this. You will feel your calf muscles and thigh muscles working in combination, which is good for toning and strengthening your legs.

Do not kick so high you have to lean forward.

◆ **Visualization**
When your hands separate at chest-level, feel you are expanding your chest and refreshing your body with clean air.

CROUCHING VARIATION

The depth of the squatting position in this movement can be varied, with recent developments of this Form making it deeper.

In martial terms, if you use the crossing of your wrists as a method for catching the ankle of an opponent's kick, by crouching lower you have more power when you straighten your legs, making it easier to throw your opponent off balance.

Flow from page 61

SEPARATE RIGHT FOOT >>

1 Straighten your left foot and place your heel on the ground, toes pointing upward. Your weight should be mostly on your right leg. Bring both your arms down in front of you so they are both straight and your fingers are pointing downward.

2 Step down with your left foot, shifting your weight. Draw your right foot in beside it, with your heel raised. Circle both hands outward and then inward until they join in front of your chest, with both palms facing toward you and your left hand closest to you. Your elbows should be bent, pointing downward, and parallel with your body.

3 Put all your weight onto your left foot. Raise your right knee to just under hip-height, extending your right thigh. Point your right foot downward. Turn your head so you are looking to the right, above your hands.

4 Slowly straighten your right leg. As you do this, move your hands apart, stretching out your right hand so it is pointing in the same direction as your foot. Draw your left hand back in line with your right hand. Both palms should be facing away from you.

strike with both fists

Strike the Ears with Both Fists is the full name for this movement and makes its martial application clear. When performing this movement, make sure your legs are in a good "Bow Stance" (see page 27), your weight is moving downward, and you are well-grounded. When you circle your arms out to the sides and then bring them around and up to the ears of an imaginary partner, the whole of your back and ribcage will lift and open. This expansion is good for the back, and the movement can be repeated as an exercise if your back is an area you would like to work on.

Bring both your fists to this position at exactly the same time.

Keep your back and shoulders relaxed

BALANCE TIP

There is a strong tendency to lean forward when doing this movement. Although your back could naturally arch here, remember to keep upright so that your center of gravity does not stray too far forward.

◆ **Visualization**
Imagine the energy for this strike beginning in your feet, traveling up your legs, and passing through your waist, along your spine, down your arms, and into your fists.

Flow from page 63

STRIKE WITH BOTH FISTS >>

1 Bring your right leg back, bent at the knee, with your toes pointing down. Bring both arms horizontally in front of you and gently curl your hands into fists.

2 Bring both your elbows into your body until they are level with your lower ribs. Bend your arms, raising your fists so they are slightly higher than your shoulders.

3 Step forward onto your right heel. Bring your fists down to hip-level, knuckles turned outward.

4 Shift your weight forward onto your right foot, making a "Bow Stance," and "strike" slowly to the temples of an imaginary opponent with the knuckles of your index fingers.

turn and separate left foot

C ontrary to the popular image of martial arts the media presents, t'ai chi does not have many kicking movements. Only two appear in this Form. They are identical but performed with alternate legs.

Practicing t'ai chi requires you to maintain a particular posture while exerting various groups of muscles, which is excellent for all-round coordination. Standing on one leg during this movement is a good example. Like Separate Right Foot, this sequence helps develop balance and stability.

◆ Visualization
Don't move as if performing an aggressive kick. Imagine that your legs are joined together and you are carefully separating them.

Straighten your back as you point your toes and push out your arms.

FLEXIBILITY VARIATION

You can vary how high you lift your knee before separating your foot. In China, it is popular to perform a very high, slow kick with apparent ease. Unless you have extremely well-developed hip and knee joints, you will not be able to do this, and it is not necessary. Simply raise your foot to the most comfortable level, keeping your balance and composure.

Traditionally the kicking leg is expected to rise above 90 degrees to the body, but the height of your kick will vary depending on how flexible you are.

Flow from page 65

TURN AND SEPARATE LEFT FOOT >>

1 Pivot to the left on the toes of both feet while turning your torso 90 degrees to the left. Lower your arms to your sides so they are spread out above your hips, with the palms facing forward.

2 Cross your hands in front of your waist and let them join at the wrists, with your left hand on top and both palms facing toward you. Turn further to the left, shifting your weight back onto your right foot, while you raise your left heel and turn your foot to the front.

3 Raise your hands to chest-height and lift your left knee, letting your lower leg hang down, toes pointed downward.

4 Straighten your left leg, stretching out your foot and pushing your left hand out so it is directly above your foot, palm facing out. Extend your right hand out to your side, to the right, at shoulder-height, palm out.

squat down

This sequence is also known as Single Whip Squatting Down or Snake Creeps Down. The movement ends in a position not otherwise found in the Yang style, so it is probably a hybrid move using elements from other Forms.

Squatting down in this position utilizes the thigh muscles in ways they are not normally used, so the Form will strengthen your thighs. It also exercises a joint called the groin crease, (called the *kua* in Chinese), which is rarely used by people living in the West, as they usually sit on chairs, instead of on the floor. The *kua* connects the torso and the legs, and its use improves circulation within the thighs and lower abdomen.

◆ **Visualization**
Feel that the movements of your two hands are completely connected. Try to synchronize them so they both arrive in the final position simultaneously.

Use your left arm to steady your balance.

MARTIAL VARIATIONS

During combat you can imagine how your left hand, jutting out in the final position, could be a hooking parry, catching or deflecting a kick.

You could also raise your left hand higher, with the palm facing forward, and bent slightly backward. This action would indicate a strike under the jaw of an opponent rather than a parry.

Flow from
page 67

SQUAT DOWN >>

GOLDEN ROOSTER

1 Move your right arm so it is pointing directly ahead of you. Make a "beak" (see page 51) with your right hand and point your left fingers toward it. Put the ball of your left foot on the floor, with your heel up. Look at your hands.

2 Step out to your left with your left heel, so your toes are pointing away from you. Most of your weight should be on your right leg.

3 Lowering your left toes onto the floor, lean your body to the left, shifting your weight. Move your left hand downward opposite your left thigh. As you do this, begin to move your right "beak" hand downward until it is slightly above shoulder-height. Bend both your knees and lower your body.

4 Straighten up into the "Bow Stance." Lift your left hand level with your face and turn in your palm so it is facing right. Lower your right arm slightly behind your back. Your "beak" hand should be behind you, pointing upward.

5 Shift your weight onto your left foot and raise your right leg. Press down beside your right thigh with your left hand, with the palm down. Opening your "beak" hand, push upward and forward until your elbow is over your right thigh.

golden rooster stands on one leg

The literal meaning of the Chinese characters for this posture is Golden Bird Alone Standing. The firmness and definition of your raised leg and arms make this one-legged stance relatively easy to accomplish with little loss of balance. Your lowered right hand lends stability while your left arm parallels your upright spine. Your left arm also represents the connection between earth and sky. Relax into this posture and hold it for a minute or so, letting your body become calm and composed.

◆ **Visualization**
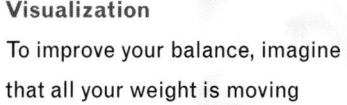
To improve your balance, imagine that all your weight is moving down your body—via your right leg—into the floor.

Use your left arm to help you balance.

MARTIAL APPLICATIONS

In a fight, the rising arm could strike an opponent in the face or neck, and the rising knee in the groin or abdomen. Holding the Golden Rooster Stands on One Leg pose is a good way to develop the necessary balance to perform kicks such as Separate Right Foot (see page 62), and Turn and Separate Left Foot (see page 66).

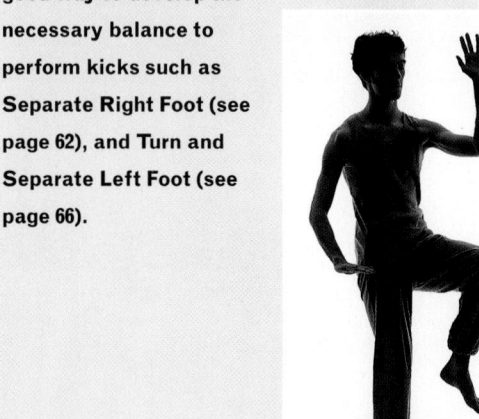

Flow from
page 69

SQUAT DOWN >>

1 Make a "beak" with your left hand and raise to your left side, level with the top of your head. Point your right fingers at your other hand, palm down.

2 Step down with your right foot and sweep your right palm down in front of your body until it is in line with your right leg, just above your right knee.

3 Shift your weight forward, beginning the "Bow Stance," pushing upward with the fingers of your right hand. Bring your "beak" hand forward, down, back, and behind your left hip. Straighten into a completed "Bow Stance."

GOLDEN ROOSTER

4 Shift all your weight onto your right foot and raise your left knee horizontally, foot pointing down. Press down beside your left thigh with your right hand, with the palm downward (see the left hand in step 5, page 69). Opening your "beak" hand, push upward, so it is upright in front of your face. Your elbow should be over your left thigh.

fair lady works with shuttles — right

The literal meaning of one of the Chinese characters in Fair Lady Works with Shuttles means "Walking Wood," which refers to a shuttle passing back and forth across a loom.

This movement is the first time in the Form when you move your whole body in a diagonal direction. The way you smoothly turn through different angles during this sequence is reminiscent of another Chinese internal martial art called Pakua, the "Art of Walking the Circle."

◆ **Visualization**

Imagine your right arm finishes up curved like a bow, and your left arm follows through straight, like an arrow.

Make sure your right hand does not obscure your eyes.

HOLD A BALL VARIATION

Instead of altering the position of the arms during steps 3 and 4, one variation is to "Hold a Ball" all through the sequence. This variation can be useful for beginners who would like to concentrate more on the position of their feet.

Flow from page 71

FAIR LADY WORKS WITH SHUTTLES — RIGHT >>

1 Lower your left heel to the ground, keeping toes raised. At the same time, turn your torso 45 degrees to the left. Move your arms inward, beginning the "Hold a Ball" position with your left hand on top.

2 Place your left foot flat on the floor and bring your right foot closer to it, heel raised. Your weight should be on your left foot. Complete the "Hold a Ball" posture so your arms are in front of your body.

3 Step out diagonally right with your right foot into the "Bow Stance." Raise your right arm across your chest, palm facing in. Place your left palm behind your right, halfway down your right forearm.

4 Shift your weight onto your right foot, raise your right arm above your forehead, turning your palm out, and push forward at chin-level with your left palm.

fair lady works
with shuttles — left

*Look directly ahead
as you complete the
movement.*

In China it is uncommon for a martial technique to be named after a woman. It is possible that the "Fair Lady" was originally some kind of goddess who could be imagined weaving the strands of Yin and Yang together in a cosmic pattern.

Fair Lady Works With Shuttles is sometimes called Four Corners, because in a different version of the Form you step to each of the four corners of an imaginary rectangle.

This movement is particularly beneficial for the waist, as well as opening and relaxing the shoulders.

◆ **Visualization**
Try to move with the delicacy and precision of someone working with a loom. Imagine the separate movements of your body are threads that you are weaving together.

MARTIAL APPLICATION

The final posture in this sequence could be used to deflect a blow to the head while striking an opponent's face with the heel of your palm. The effect of your strike is enhanced by your whole body moving forward at the same time. This is a good example of how t'ai chi moves can exhibit both the principles of Yin (guiding the opponent's strike away) and Yang (your own strike) at the same time.

Flow from page 73

FAIR LADY WORKS WITH SHUTTLES — LEFT >>

1 Bend your left knee and move your weight back onto your left foot. Bring your right hand around in front of you. Look at your palm. Lower your left hand and put it under your right forearm, palm up.

2 Shift your weight onto your right foot. Lower your arms, still in the same position, to your waist. Then move your left foot up beside your right, heel raised.

3 Step diagonally left into the "Bow Stance" with your left foot. Raise your left arm in front of your chest, palm facing inward, and lift your right hand so you are pointing toward your left hand.

4 Complete the movement by shifting your weight onto your left foot as you straighten your right leg. At the same time, raise your left arm above your forehead, palm facing out, and push through at chin-height with your right arm. Look directly ahead.

needle at sea bottom

This is one of the few movements in t'ai chi where you bend forward out of the normal vertical position. As it is generally followed by Fan Penetrates Back, you experience a low bending movement followed by a high, wide, opening movement—Yin followed by Yang. Needle At Sea Bottom benefits the pelvic region and the abdominal muscles.

This movement can be used martially to release a grip on your right wrist. The final downward push makes it difficult for an assailant to keep hold of your wrist. The movement opens up a weak point in his or her grip and pushes the hand away.

◆ **Visualization**
Imagine your right hand is a needle that you are thrusting down into the sea. Feel your energy being concentrated into one small space.

Keep your back as straight as possible during this movement.

FINGER POSITION VARIATION

The position of the supporting fingers of the left hand can be altered, as they can in the Press movement seen earlier in the Form. One reason why these positions may vary is because a particular practitioner or teacher decides to reinforce the chi through a particular place on the wrist or arm.

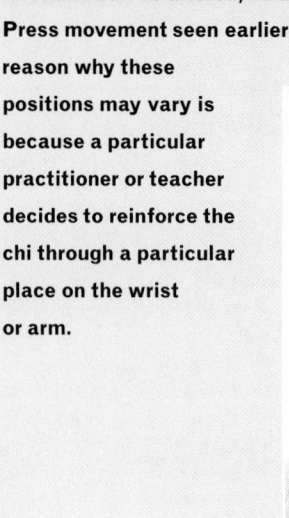

Flow from page 75

NEEDLE AT SEA BOTTOM >>

1 Shift more of your weight onto your left foot, and draw your right foot a little closer to your left, heel raised. Bring your left hand down opposite your chin and your right hand to your abdomen.

2 Step back with your right foot and place your weight upon it while raising your left heel. Turn your waist to the right. Lower your left hand to just above waist-height and bend your right arm inward, lifting it to shoulder-height with your palm turned inward.

3 Turn your waist back to the left. Bring your right palm closer to your face as you lower your left hand toward your left thigh. Look down in front of you.

4 Still keeping most of your weight on your right leg, bend forward from your waist, reaching downward with the fingers of your right hand. Look at your right hand.

fan penetrates back

Keep your head aligned with your spine.

A war fan, made of metal, was a common weapon in the East. In this sequence you should imagine you are moving like a fan: opening, closing, spreading, and contracting. Your arms are spreading your chi as they separate from one another. Your spine conducts energy up, down, and around itself. The "fan" allows this energy to spread throughout your upper body and arms and around your head.

Let the actions of your arms lift up your chest during this movement. This raises your ribcage, enabling you to breathe more deeply and easily. This action of raising your arms and opening your chest continues in the next sequence, Turn and Chop.

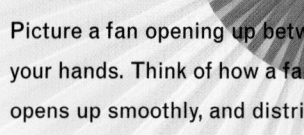

◆ Visualization
Picture a fan opening up between your hands. Think of how a fan opens up smoothly, and distribute your energy in the same even way.

MARTIAL VARIATIONS

The height of your right hand and the degree to which it is pulled back beside your head can vary in this posture. In addition, the position of your left hand, how much it is bent, or whether it is turned side-on, can vary. The reasons for these differences could be due to defensive applications. For example, instead of your two hands striking an opponent, you could be defending against a high blow to your head.

Flow from
page 77

FAN PENETRATES BACK >>

1 Bring your body back upward, keeping your weight distributed evenly on both legs. Push your right hand up in front of your chin, with the palm in and the fingers pointing away from your face. Your left hand is in front of your face, with palm facing out and fingers pointing upward.

2 Step further left with your left leg into the "Bow Stance." Push your left hand out in front of you and pull your right hand closer to your face, lifting your elbow behind your head so your palm is facing away from you.

turn and chop

One of the Chinese characters for this action indicates the movement made in rowing a boat, which is a useful way to remember how to move in this sequence. This movement is good for developing flexibility, as it stretches your body from your extended right front fist, through your arm, across your chest, over your left shoulder, and down to your left wrist and palm.

Remember to turn your left foot 90 degrees as you begin. Forgetting to do this can make things difficult, as your legs will be in an awkward position for the beginning of the next movement, Parry and Punch.

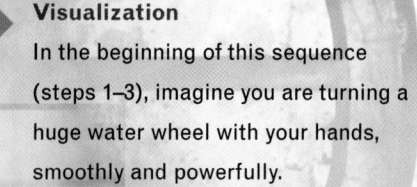

◆ **Visualization**
In the beginning of this sequence (steps 1–3), imagine you are turning a huge water wheel with your hands, smoothly and powerfully.

_____ *Follow your hands with your gaze.*

MARTIAL APPLICATION

In a combative scenario, your left palm would press down to drive off an attempt to grip your right elbow (see step 2, below). Also, your right hand could be used to make a "back fist" strike (a blow from the side using the back of the fist) at an imaginary opponent's chin (see step 4, below).

Flow from page 79

>>> **TURN AND CHOP** >>

1 Turn your left foot inward 90 degrees. Shift your weight back onto your left foot and step around with your right foot so your feet are parallel. Bring both hands over to your right, with your right hand higher than your head and your left hand coming across at face-height. Twist to the right and look between your arms.

2 Make a "soft" fist with your right hand and bring your arm down until your fist is level with your abdomen. Move your left arm downward behind you to hip-height. Pull your right foot in closer to your left, heel raised.

3 Lift your right leg off the floor so your thigh is horizontal. Press down with your left palm beside your right elbow. Look straight ahead.

4 Put your right heel down and bring your right fist across to make a "back fist" strike at an imaginary opponent's chin, pulling your left palm closer to your body.

parry and punch

Chop, Parry, and Punch are usually described as one movement, but have been divided into two sequences here for ease of presentation. Your hand is in a fist, but it is not tense, nor are you moving with aggressive energy. Think of it is as a "soft fist": gently closed and moving with the same controlled feeling used throughout the Form.

The opening of your chest experienced in the last two sequences continues during this one. As your left hand pushes forward and your right hand is drawn back into your hips (see step 2, below), notice how this stretches your waist, torso, and chest.

Visualization
Pretend you are deflecting an incoming punch with your left, open palm and that you follow this up with a punch.

At the end of the sequence, concentrate on keeping your balance and maintaining a strong posture.

JING APPLICATION

When performing this movement, some practitioners circle their right hand around their right kidney to induce *jing*. Jing is the sending out of chi or the conversion of chi into applied force that is expelled from the body. It can be used both in a martial context and in healing.

Flow from
page 81

PARRY AND PUNCH >>

1 Shift your weight onto your right foot. Turn your body to the right and lift your left heel, pushing forward with your left palm and pulling your right fist back toward your hip.

2 Step forward with your left foot into the "Bow Stance," placing your heel on the floor and raising your toes. At the same time, push forward with your left hand.

3 Shift your weight onto your left foot and punch horizontally forward at chest-height with your right hand. As you do this, bring your left hand toward your right forearm with your fingers pointing upward and the palm facing inward, lightly touching your right arm.

withdraw and push, as if closing a door

The second half of this sequence, As if Closing a Door, mirrors the movement needed to close a sliding door. In As if Closing a Door you reach out to collect the chi, which has been brought in, generated, and spread about by the practice of the Form. In the next posture, Cross Hands, you bring the chi into the centre of your body.

Let the movement of your arms naturally expand your chest.

◆ Visualization
Imagine you are collecting chi from the air and bringing it into your *dantien*.

POSTURE VARIATION

The chief variation is in the distance with which you reach to the side with your right hand, and in how much you twist your body back to the left, prior to moving back to center for Cross Hands.

Flow from page 83

WITHDRAW AND PUSH >>

1 Turn your left palm downward and slide it underneath your right forearm. Turn both palms upward simultaneously away from your body, then draw them apart. Move your weight onto your right foot.

2 Pull your palms back to your body, bending your elbow. Keep most of your weight on your right foot. Turn your palms to face away from your body, fingers pointing diagonally away from you and upward.

3 Shifting your weight onto your front foot, push downward and upward so that your arms are almost fully straightened, but not locked.

AS IF CLOSING A DOOR >>

4 Move your weight onto your right foot and turn your torso to the right. Raise your right palm, facing outward, level with your forehead. At the same time, move your left arm across your body so that your arms are spread apart.

5 Begin to shift your weight back onto your left foot. Move your right arm further out to the right side of your body, and straighten your left arm. Your arms should be spread out with your left hand lower than your right.

cross hands and close form

The characters for this closing posture include the symbols for the number ten, a child under a roof, and a hand. The child under a roof evokes a feeling of stability, peace, and rectitude. The character for ten is in the form of a cross, which can be seen as indicating the four primary directions of north, south, east, and west.

In this final position you return, refreshed and replenished, to the original posture that began the Form. Chi has been spread throughout your body, your channels have been opened, and your spirit lifted. You return to a state of *wu-wei*—non-action.

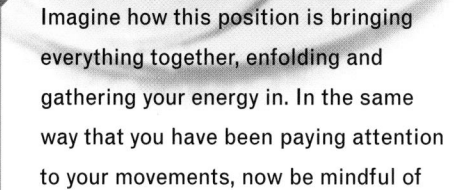

◆ **Visualization**
Imagine how this position is bringing everything together, enfolding and gathering your energy in. In the same way that you have been paying attention to your movements, now be mindful of the sensation of stillness.

MARTIAL VARIATION

You can bend very low down, almost into a squat, before rising into the completed posture. This improves leg strength and emphasizes the combative aspect: your crossed arms could catch an opponent's ankle during a kicking attack and lift him or her off balance.

Make sure your feet are parallel before you lift your hands.

Flow from page 85

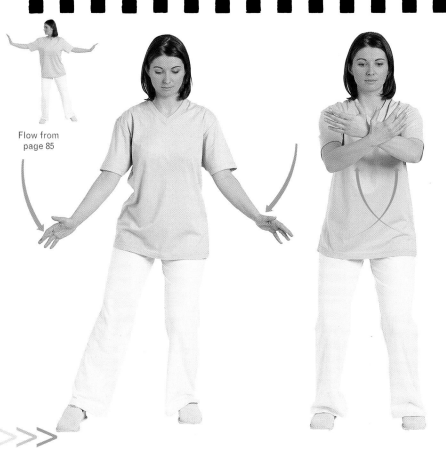

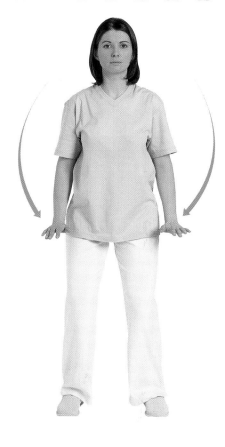

CROSS HANDS >>

1 Simultaneously lower both your arms to cross in front of your lower abdomen and bring your right foot back so that it is parallel with your left.

2 Raise your arms to a crossed position in front of your chest, with your right hand in front and your elbows down and palms facing in. Look down across the tops of your hands.

CLOSE FORM >>

3 Move your hands apart so your upper arms are horizontal and your elbows are pointing out. Press down slowly, bringing your arms to your sides. Straighten your legs.

4 Gently bring your hands down to hip-height. Relax and maintain the posture for a minute or so, letting your energy settle and your mind rest.

"When under attack, be calm,
And comprehend movement in stillness.
The way you give way to an opponent,
Will fill him with wonder."

From "Song of the Thirteen Postures"

In Push Hands we study how not to meet force with opposing force. Instead, we yield to the force, moving with its power, and then use this power to overcome the opponent. This is a vital t'ai chi principle and one that has physical, mental, and spiritual relevance.

4

>> applications with a partner

single push hands

Push Hands is a t'ai chi exercise performed with another person that enables you to become sensitive to his or her balance and energy and how he or she interacts with your own. It is an effective way to practice movements that utilize chi instead of relying on muscular force. It also demonstrates how to apply t'ai chi during martial situations.

Push Hands is like a physical dialogue of pressure and withdrawal between two people, so you need to be sensitive not only to your own body but to the posture and movements of your partner. You are not trying to win an argument with your partner, you are trying to communicate with him or her. Being able to control or unbalance your partner is not the aim.

During Push Hands you move with whatever force is used against you. In moving with your partner's force, you prevent his or her energy being used against you. This is because if there is no resistance to a force, then that force has nothing to act against and cannot be applied.

It is essential to remain calm and relaxed during Push Hands. This can be extremely difficult to do, as our habitual response to being pushed or moved around by someone is to tense up and resist. However, after sufficient practice, Push Hands enables us to have a different attitude and response.

"If others don't move, I don't move" (Lo, Inn, and Amacker, *The Essence of T'ai Chi Ch'uan*) is the correct attitude for Push Hands and for the ethos of t'ai chi in general. A popular name among t'ai chi practitioners for this attitude is "yielding." It is believed that once you are proficient at yielding, you cannot be overcome by brute force.

practicing single push hands

This version of Push Hands is performed by two partners standing opposite each other in the "Bow Stance," with their right arms outstretched in the Ward Off position and their left hands near their right elbows. One partner gently connects his or her palm with, and gently pushes against, the wrist of the second, who in turn softens the wrist and lowers the elbow, thereby receiving and re-directing the energy of the push. They then swap roles, still using their right hands, with the second now pushing, and the first yielding. The entire sequence is then repeated, becoming one smooth, circular, and continuous movement.

Remember, Push Hands is not merely a martial technique. The concept of yielding and giving way, yet still remaining in control, has relevance to all human interactions, not just combat.

SINGLE PUSH HANDS

In this version of Push Hands each partner only uses one hand. On page 93 you can see the more advanced version, Double Push Hands.

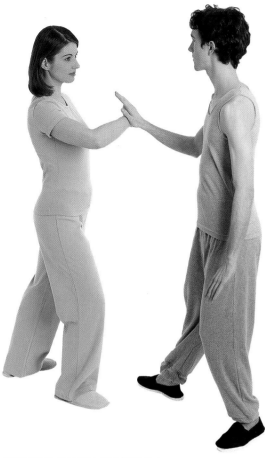

SINGLE PUSH HANDS >>

1 Stand facing one another in the "Bow Stance." Partner 2 (on the right, above) places his palm on the back of partner 1's wrist, as shown. Partner 2's body weight is back on his left leg, and partner 1's weight is forward on her right leg. Both partners should support their arms and not lean or rest them on those of the other person.

2 Partner 2 moves his weight forward onto his right foot, keeping a firm contact with partner 1's wrist. Sensing this pressure, partner 1 moves her whole body backward, at the same time turning her hand outward, and twisting it, to divert partner 2's push away from the center of her body.

3 When partner 2 has completed his forward movement, his weight is now on his right foot and partner 1's weight is on her left foot. Partner 1's right hand is now resting on the back of partner 2's hand, below the knuckles. She then pushes against him and he gives way, preventing her from obtaining any leverage. Both partners then repeat steps 1–3, having alternated roles at the end of the sequence.

double push hands

Like Single Push Hands, Double Push Hands is performed by two partners standing in the "Bow Stance." The movement begins in the same way as Single Push Hands, with one partner gently pushing against the other's wrist. However, when the yielding partner begins to bend the elbow, then the partner who is pushing places his or her left hand against the yielding partner's elbow and guides the whole arm with both hands. Again, the yielding partner accepts the force, and then they change roles.

combat applications

By learning to move with a partner's force in Push Hands, you can prepare yourself for applying one of the fundamental tenets of t'ai chi in combat—perceiving the intentions behind your opponent's movements, following his or her direction, and then using the person's force against him or her. In the examples on the right, you can see how partner 1 uses partner 2's energy to unbalance him, making him vulnerable to a subsequent strike. Remember when applying these strikes that the power for any movements in t'ai chi should originate from your feet, move through your legs and waist, and be expressed in the rest of your body, or focused into one specific movement (for example the chop in step 1, right).

PUSH HANDS AND CHOP

1 Notice that in step 2 of the Double Push Hands exercise (see page 93), partner 1's right hand is turning over the surface of partner 2's right wrist. If, instead of keeping her fingers open, she were to seize his wrist and pull it forward, she could then chop the back of his neck.

PUSH HANDS AND PUNCH

2 She could also pull his arm with both her hands and then, as he is bent forward, release her left hand and punch him underneath his ribs.

DOUBLE PUSH HANDS >>

1 Take up the same positions you had at the beginning of Single Push Hands (see page 91), with both partners in the "Bow Stance," and partner 2 (on the right, above) connecting his right hand to partner 1's wrist.

2 As partner 2 pushes forward, he places his free left hand on partner 1's elbow. As he pushes, she raises her left hand in front of her body, ready to receive his elbow.

3 Partner 1 then pushes forward and to her right with both hands, and partner 2 yields, turning his right wrist away and letting his elbow move in the same direction as her left hand.

4 As partner 1 pushes forward, partner 2 leans back and takes his left hand away from her elbow. When partner 1 has completed the push forward, partner 1 begins to push back, and the sequence begins again, from step 1.

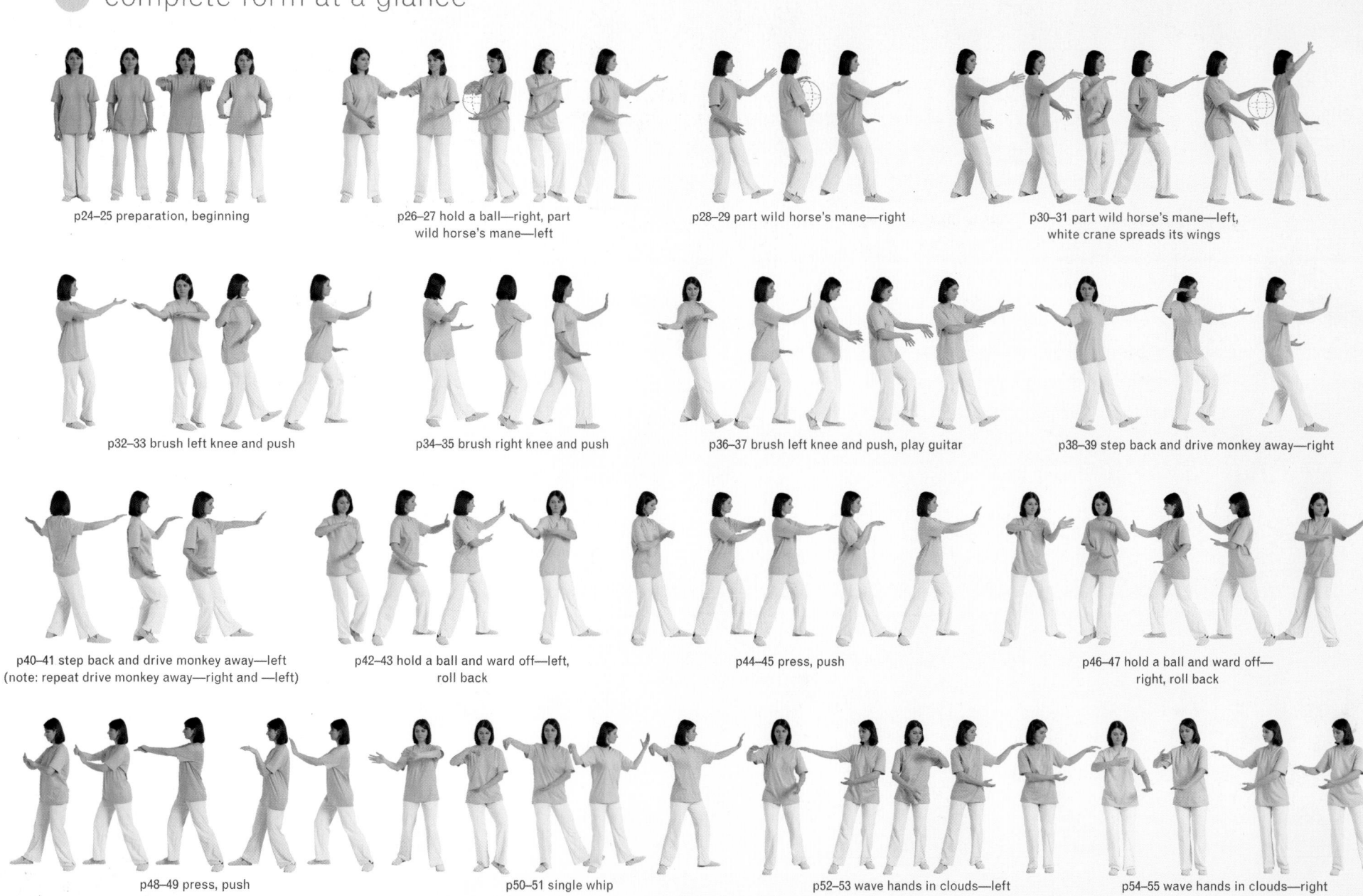

p24–25 preparation, beginning

p26–27 hold a ball—right, part
wild horse's mane—left

p28–29 part wild horse's mane—right

p30–31 part wild horse's mane—left,
white crane spreads its wings

p32–33 brush left knee and push

p34–35 brush right knee and push

p36–37 brush left knee and push, play guitar

p38–39 step back and drive monkey away—right

p40–41 step back and drive monkey away—left
(note: repeat drive monkey away—right and —left)

p42–43 hold a ball and ward off—left,
roll back

p44–45 press, push

p46–47 hold a ball and ward off—
right, roll back

p48–49 press, push

p50–51 single whip

p52–53 wave hands in clouds—left

p54–55 wave hands in clouds—right

p56–57 wave hands in clouds—left

p58–59 wave hands in clouds—right

p60–61 single whip, high pat on horse

p62–63 separate right foot

p64–65 strike with both fists

p66–67 turn and separate left foot

p68–69 squat down, golden
rooster stands on one leg

p70–71 squat down, golden rooster
stands on one leg

p72–73 fair lady works
with shuttles—right

p74–75 fair lady works
with shuttles—left

p76–77 needle at sea bottom

p78–79 fan penetrates back

p80–81 turn and chop

p82–83 parry and punch

p84–85 withdraw and push, as if closing a door

p86–87 cross hands and close form

complete form at a glance

Index

Arm Swing 16

As if Closing a Door 84–85

Beginning 24–25

"Bow Stance," the 13, 27, 29, 31, 33, 35, 37, 42, 47, 51, 61, 64, 65, 69, 71, 73, 75, 79, 83, 90, 91, 92, 93

Brush Left Knee and Push 32–33

Brush Left Knee and Push (repeat) 36–37

Brush Right Knee and Push 34–35

Chi 4, 10, 11, 16, 22, 28, 44, 52, 54, 56, 58, 60, 78, 82, 84, 86

Close Form 86–87

Clothing 5

Cross Hands 86–87

Dantiens 10, 11, 30, 56

Double Push Hands 89, 92–93

Fair Lady Works with Shuttles—Left 74–75

Fair Lady Works with Shuttles—Right 72–73

Fan Penetrates Back 78–79

Feng shui 10

Focusing the mind 4, 15

Folding Wings 20–21

Golden Rooster Stands on One Leg 69, 70–71

Golden Rooster Stands on One Leg (repeat) 70–71

Grasp the Bird's Tail 42, 46, 48

Gravity Back Stretch 17

Hand positions 12, 20, 50, 51, 61, 69, 71

High Pat on Horse 60–61

"Hold a Ball" 26–27, 29, 31, 43, 47, 51, 53, 55, 57, 72, 73

"Hold a Ball" and Ward Off—Left 42–43

"Hold a Ball" and Ward Off—Right 46–47

Jing 82

Junction points 10, 11

Kua 20, 68

Lao–gong 11, 52

Ming–men 11, 40

Needle at Sea Bottom 76–77

Opening and closing 13

Pace 24

Parry and Punch 82–83

Part Wild Horse's Mane— Left 27, 31

Part Wild Horse's Mane— Left (repeat) 31

Part Wild Horse's Mane— Right 28–29

Play Guitar 36–37

Posture 12, 24

Preparation 24–25

Press 42, 44–45

Press (repeat) 48–49

Push 42, 44–45

Push (repeat) 48–49

Relaxation 10, 12, 15, 16, 18–19, 56

Roll Back 42, 43, 46–47

Separate Right Foot 62–63

Single Push Hands 89, 90–91, 92

Single Whip 50–51, 61

"Song of the Thirteen Postures" 8, 14, 22, 88

Squat Down 68–69, 71

Squat Down (repeat) 70–71

Step Back and Drive Monkey Away—Left 40–41

Step Back and Drive Monkey Away—Right 38–39, 41

Stress management 4, 10

Strike with Both Fists 64–65

T'ai chi 66, 68, 74, 76, 78, 80, 82,

health benefits of 4, 9, 10, 24, 28, 30, 34, 38, 40, 46, 54, 60, 62, 64

history of 6–7

martial applications of 10, 30, 38, 46, 48, 54, 62, 68, 70, 74, 78, 80, 86, 90, 92

Taoism 6, 30

Tension 12

The Ten Essentials 56, 58

"Tiger's Mouth," the 12, 29

Turn and Chop 80–81

Turn and Separate Left Foot 66–67

Visualization 56

Wave Hands in Clouds— Left 52–53

Wave Hands in Clouds— Left (repeat) 57

Wave Hands in Clouds— Right 54–55

Wave Hands in Clouds— Right (repeat) 59

Where to practice t'ai chi 5

White Crane Spreads its Wings 30–31

Withdraw and Push 84–85

Yin and Yang 10, 12, 13, 24, 32, 38, 40, 44, 60, 74, 76

ACKNOWLDGEMENTS

The author would like to acknowledge the following people and titles for their help in different ways to the appearance of this book: Dr. Cheng Man-ch'ing, whom I never met, but who inspired all of us. My first teacher John, who always prefers to be anonymous. Miss Theresa Yang, for teaching me the Wu Form. Mr Ho Bun Yuen, for his help in approaching Chinese Wushu. Dr Ji from Taiwan, whose full name was never given out. Mr Ji Jian Cheng, for Pakua and injecting new life into my studies. Lama Zangmo, for helping me through a difficult time. Michelle Bernard and Stuart Moorhouse, without whose marvelous assistance at Carroll and Brown this book would never have met its deadline! Not forgetting Amy for giving me the opportunity in the first place and Jules and Justin for the marvelous lunches...

Jane Schorre, *How To Grasp the Bird's Tail If You Don't Speak Chinese*, North Atlantic Books, 1997.

Fu Zhongwen, *Mastering Yang Style Taijiquan*, North Atlantic Books, 1999.

Dr Yang Jwing-ming, *T'ai Chi Theory and Martial Power*, YMAA Publication Center, 1997.

Howard Thomas, *T'ai Chi Training in China*, Paul H. Crompton Ltd, 1997.

Benjamin Lo, et al, *The Essence of T'ai Chi Chuan*, North Atlantic Books, 1979.

Picture Research

Sandra Schneider

Picture Credits

7 Getty Images, **30** Getty Images, **72** Getty Images

Model

Rafaella Baruzzo